THE HATCHETT DIARY

THE
HATCHETT DIARY

A tour through the counties of England and Scotland
in 1796
visiting their mines and manufactories

edited and with an introduction by
ARTHUR RAISTRICK

D. BRADFORD BARTON LTD
TRURO

First published 1967 by

D. BRADFORD BARTON LTD

FRANCES STREET TRURO CORNWALL

Printed by
H. E. WARNE LTD. ST. AUSTELL

CONTENTS

ROUTE OF CHARLES HATCHETT'S TOUR APRIL 26 TO AUGUST 14, 1796

FOREWORD

The diary of Charles Hatchett's travels here printed is written in five small quarto books 8 ins. × 6½ ins., four of them having 56 pages and one of 72 pages. They are closely written to every edge of the page, entries being made on each day of the journey. The diaries were preserved by his grand-daughter Lucy Catherine and from her they descended to Miss Hatchett-Jackson who between 1944 and 1947 gave them to her cousin, a great-great-grand-daughter of Charles Hatchett, and they were kept among her husband's papers. Some years after his death his daughter in 1965 gave them to Mrs. Anita Hatchett, widow of Charles Hatchett's great-great-grandson.

It is through Mrs. Hatchett's interest and generosity that they have been made available for publication. I am greatly indebted to her not only for the privilege of studying and transcribing the diaries, but also for the great help given by references from her own work on the life of Charles Hatchett and from the diaries of his journeys on the Continent and in Russia which form the basis of her own study of this remarkable man.

Hatchett's journey was made at a time of great ferment in the world of mechanics and engineering. The Industrial Revolution was well under way, Boulton and Watt's condensing steam engine was successfully applied to textile and other machinery, and the mining world had already embarked on a new era made possible by the use of Newcomen's engine in pumping. The iron industry had discovered iron as a structural material and new ways of making steel had been adopted. These all attracted Hatchett's attention but it was in smelting houses and chemical works that his basic interest in chemistry came to the fore, alongside his deep interest in mineralogy.

The geological world had been stirred by the theories of Werner (1749-1817) who derived all rocks by a process of aqueous deposition and who had also some important ideas on the formation of mineral veins, their character and content. In August 1791 Hatchett met Werner at Freiberg and saw the School of Mines of which he was Principal; it may have been then that he became acquainted with Savaresi who also visited Werner in 1789 and stayed a long time in Freiberg. When Hatchett arrived in Edinburgh he found himself at the heart of a growing controversy. The Edinburgh 'school' of Natural Philosophers was divided; some like Jameson were ardent Wernerians, others followed Hutton and were formulating new theories in opposition. Hatchett entered into all this, visited the classic sites and noted in detail the evidence on which arguments were being based. He attended lectures, dined with members of the University, and took Jameson with him across Scotland. No doubt they argued and discussed the controversial 'whin stone' at quarries and exposures wherever they could find them.

Hatchett was very critical of the mineral collections at Edinburgh and Glasgow, but remembering that in all his journeys through Russia, Germany and this country he had visited every 'cabinet' of minerals to which he could get access and was himself an experienced collector and accomplished mineralogist, his criticisms must carry considerable weight.

The diary at once recalls the earlier one of the French mining engineer Gabriel Jars, who visited England and Scotland between 1758 and 1767, and in 1781 published his three volume *Voyages Metallurgiques* with his observations on mines and on industries connected particularly with the production of iron. A closer contemporary was Faujas St. Fond (1742-1819) whose *Voyages en Angleterre, en Ecosse, et aux Iles Hebrides* was published in 1797, and which covered some of the same ground as Hatchett's journey. The two did not meet but Hatchett quotes some of St. Fond's conclusions about basalts, which he drew from the work on ancient volcanoes in France which St. Fond had published in 1778.

Hatchett set out from London with letters of introduction to some of the important people in the mining areas, and accompanied by them, made observations on mines and smelting houses, mineral collections, steam engines and everything connected with mining. He collected and also bought minerals, and wrote May 23, 1796, to the Hon. Charles Greville[1] that he had got for him "a tolerable

---

[1] Hon. Charles Francis Greville (1749-1809) was second son of the first Earl of Warwick and had formed one of the finest collections of minerals ever gathered together. He was invited to become the patron of the newly formed Geological Society.

Hatchett wrote to him from Bath but does not say where he collected the fluors. He goes on to say "I have also got for you a specimen of the Crystallized Vitreous Copper Ore of Cooks Kitchen, but not equal to what has formerly been found as it is now very scarce.—I could not for any money tempt the Miners to descend into Huel Rock for the Sulphurated Tin, for they assured me that it was impracticable."

suite of the Cornish Fluors, from the Cube to the 24 sided crystal which I know you have not at present." The style of the diary is fresh and direct, easy to read and gripping because of the obvious interest of the writer in all that he saw and heard. All his observations are acute and factual. The travelling was done by post chaise and the cost of every mile is recorded with that of meals, inns, tips, etc., all of which was shared equally with Savaresi. His running commentary on the countryside towns and people gives a good picture of travel at that time. Notes on the country range little beyond 'open, fertile, hilly, barren' or a brief comment of that sort. Occasionally he ventures on the romantic or picturesque. He notes carefully the material used as road stone and stopped to examine roadside exposures, and from these he put together a good general outline of the geology of the country he crossed.

Savaresi, the Italian mineralogist, shared his journey as far as Edinburgh, and made some contribution to discussions of minerals and geology, but not to industrial topics. The letters which Hatchett carried and the people with whom he dined and visited give the impression that he was welcomed as a mineralogist and geologist of some standing. At all stages of his journey the people he met were glad to furnish forward introductions, and the people to whom he presented his letters found him of sufficient importance to spend two or three days with him, arrange meetings with other people of scientific or industrial standing and get facilities for him to visit works, mines and collieries. In Edinburgh he was proposed and accepted as a member of the Royal Society of Edinburgh.

From Lead Hills in Scotland his return journey is more hurried, and after a few days of illness at Chester and a visit at Shrewsbury from Dr. Darwin junr. he made no more visits but travelled by the quickest way to London.

My thanks are tendered to Dr. C. D. Waterson and Miss Sweet, both of the Royal Scottish Museum, who have provided me with notes on the people whom Hatchett met in Scotland; also to Mrs. R. M. Barton for the map she has provided, and to her husband Mr. D. B. Barton for help and advice in the preparation of the diary for publication.

ARTHUR RAISTRICK

Linton, Skipton
1967

CHARLES HATCHETT F.R.S. (1766 - 1847)

CHARLES HATCHETT was born 2nd January 1766, the only child of John and Elizabeth Hatchett of Long Acre, London. His father was a coach maker of sufficient repute to be appointed coach maker to the Tsarina Catherine II of Russia. Of Charles's education we know nothing but at the time of his marriage to Elizabeth Collick, in 1787, he was active in the coachmaking business, without having served a craft apprenticeship. At some time he acquired a knowledge of chemistry and a great interest in mineralogy and the analysis of minerals. In 1790 his father sent a coach to Catherine of Russia and Charles went to St. Petersburg to deliver this personally and also call upon many of the Russian and Continental aristocracy to secure their interest in the Hatchett coaches. He met many famous people and among others dined with the king of Poland. Whatever his scientific training had been it was of such quality that Sir Joseph Banks gave him letters of introduction to Dr. Pallas [1] then in St. Petersburg, and encouraged him to call on other scientists on his journey across the Continent.

In September 1790, on his way to Russia, Hatchett was in Berlin where he called upon Professor Klaproth [2] and "found him a pleasant man". Klaproth only the year before had discovered the new element which he named Uranium and Hatchett was of sufficient standing as a chemist for Klaproth to present to him "some Uranium Nitratum, but could not give me any of the regulus as his own specimen was very small . . ." The regulus was later proved to be an oxide of uranium and the pure metal was not isolated until 1841, by Pekigot. In St. Petersburg he met Pallas and was introduced by him to many

[1] Pierre Simon Pallas (1741-1811). When Catherine II of Russia ordered the Academy of Sciences to prepare an expedition to observe the Transit of Venus in 1769, which was also to make a geological, biological and sociological survey of part of Siberia, Pallas was appointed as its leader. They left St. Petersburg in June 1768 and returned in July 1774. He discovered the remains of mammoth and other extinct animals, made observations on the origin of mountains and also described the "Siberian red lead" (crocoite), found in the Beresof gold mines.

[2] Martin Heinrich Klaproth (1743-1817). A distinguished chemist and mineral analyst. He was the discoverer of uranium and verified the discoveries of tellurium and titanium. Became the first Professor of Chemistry on the foundation of the University of Berlin.

important people including Peter Demidoff[1], one of the great family of ironmasters and mine owners, through whom and through Pallas, he was enabled to visit mines and collections of minerals in St. Petersburg and in and around Moscow.

Returning from Russia by way of Warsaw in 1791 he travelled with a Mr. Titius and on to Freiberg. In his diary of the journey he says "on approaching Freiberg the smell of Sulphur etc. of the Furnaces very perceptible . . . There is a Seminary for the instruction of Students in Mineralogy to the number of about 100. Mr. Werner[2] and Mr. Charpentier are at the head of it, the latter also superintends the Amalgamation of the Ore after the improved Method of Mr. Born[3]. Introduced to Mr. Werner, reckon'd one of the first mineralogists, went to Cabinet of Minerals used in lectures, and also saw Models of Mines, Machines etc., went to one of the Mines, saw the Mode of breaking the best sort of Ore to separate it from the stoney particles by Boys with hammers . . . met (at the mine) two English Men, Students, Messrs Weaver and Barker in their Miner's Dresses. Call on Mr. Charpentier, receiv'd very politely, gave me an order for all the Masters of Mines to let me see everything."

The meeting with Werner no doubt inspired and stimulated the great interest he displayed in the North of England and in Scotland, in the 'whin stone' and in its nature and origin. It is likely that it was at Freiberg that he met Andre Savaresi (1762-1810) who was his companion on the English journey of 1796. Savaresi was born in Naples and trained in medicine but developed an interest in mineralogy. In 1789 he was sent by the king of Naples to study with Werner and to learn all he could about mines, metallurgy and the teaching of mining science. He stayed a long time in Freiberg then travelled in other parts of Germany and Poland.

When Hatchett returned to England he developed his chemical

1 Peter Demidoff, a member of the famous family of Demidoff who for some generations were ironmasters and owners of mines. It was in their mines at Nischne-Tagilsk that much of the famous Russian malachite was got. Also their mines near Sverdlovsk, south of Ekaterinburg in the Urals, was the place where platinum was discovered in 1819.

2 Abraham Gottlob Werner (1749-1817). Appointed in 1775 as Inspector and Teacher of Mining and Mineralogy in the Freiberg Academy. At the time of Hatchett's visit he was just publishing his theory of mineral veins, *Neue Theorie von der Entstehung der Gangen*, 1791, and must have stimulated Hatchett's keen observation of veins.

3 Ignaz Edler von Born (1742-1791). Transylvanian metallurgist, mineralogist and mining engineer. Inventor of the Amalgamation process for recovering gold and silver from mixed ores.

and mineralogical work and in 1794 visited mines in Devon but unfortunately no details of that tour have survived except that he examined the Bovey coals.

Hatchett's earliest published work was his paper on the "Analyses of the Carinthian Molybdate of Lead" in the Philosophical Transactions of the Royal Society (**86.** 285-339). This paper established his position as a mineral chemist and on the 9th March 1797, the Certificate of Candidature for the Fellowship of the Royal Society quoted this paper and described him as "a Gentleman distinguished for his acquirements in Natural Knowledge particularly in Chemistry and Mineralogy . . . etc." The signatories included the astronomer Herschel. This work arose from Hatchett's visit to Klaproth who had made an analysis of this mineral but from insufficient material. The mineral was recognised by Klaproth as a molybdate but its discoverer, after whom it was named *Wulfenite*, the Abbe F.X. Wulfen, thought it to be the tungstate of lead. Hatchett's analysis by its completeness finally settled the nature of this mineral.

This first paper was followed by others which included some on organic materials and Thomson[1] in 1810 described him as one of the first chemists in the organic field. Hatchett had lived in Hammersmith until near the turn of the century when he started a small manufacturing chemical business near Chiswick. There he had a laboratory and took into it a youth, an apothecary's apprentice, Thomas Brande (1788-1866), teaching him chemistry and mineralogy. Brande in 1818 married Hatchett's second daughter Anna Frederica. He became a very able chemist and later succeeded Davy as Professor at the Royal Institution, as well as an F.R.S. and a member of the Council of the Geological Society.

About the end of the century the government was disturbed by the decreasing weight of the gold coins in circulation and the Privy Council in 1798 appointed Henry Cavendish and Charles Hatchett "to ascertain whether this loss was occasioned by any defect". Cavendish devised an apparatus to measure the loss of weight when coins were rubbed together, while Hatchett investigated the alloys of gold with a long series of metals. He made binary alloys with gold and arsenic, bismuth, antimony, zinc, cobalt, nickel, manganese, lead, tin, platinum, copper and silver, and decided that

---

[1] Thomas Thomson (1773-1852). Chemist and author of a *History of Chemistry* 3 vols. 1832. Professor of Chemistry at Glasgow University 1818-1846.

only copper and silver were suitable alloys with gold for the purpose of its use in coinage. The report was completed by Hatchett alone, in April 1801.

Hatchett was engaged in arranging the mineral collection in the British Museum, particularly those minerals collected by Sir Hans Sloane, when he came across a mineral specimen sent to Sloane by Winthrop of Massachusetts, the grandson of Governor John Winthrop of Connecticut, (1606-1676). Hatchett took a portion for analysis and discovered in it a new element which he named *Columbium*. The complexity of the mineral columbite which he analysed was such as to emphasise in striking fashion the great skill and power in analysis which enabled him to discover a new element in a mineral which also contained compounds of tantalum, titanium, tungsten, zirconium, thorium, cerium and yttrium. The paper "An analysis of a mineral substance from North America containing a metal hitherto unknown" was printed in the Philosophical Transactions (**92**. 49-66) and greatly enhanced his reputation.

After 1804, the date of this paper, he published little and infrequent scientific work, though there are indications that his interest in science continued, for in 1813 he published a method of separating iron and manganese whilst in 1823 he was elected Correspondent of the Academie des Sciences. His last publication was a small quarto brochure on *"The Spikenard of the Ancients"* in 1836. He was a member of the *Literary Club* founded by Dr. Johnson and was its treasurer for many years. The *Animal Chemistry Club* met at his home and in these two clubs he was the associate of many prominent literary and scientific figures of the early nineteenth century.

There are conflicting statements which suggest that early in the new century Hatchett lost his interest in scientific work. Sir Benjamin Brodie says of the *Animal Chemistry Club* that it existed for ten or eleven years but that "Hatchett, who has now inherited a considerable fortune on the death of his father, had ceased to work in chemistry, in spite of the remonstrance of Sir Joseph Banks". Berzelius[1] who stayed with him on his London visit says "although a famous chemist at the time of his father's death, has continued to carry on the business (of coachmaker). He has a very well equipped

---

[1] Jons Jacob Berzelius (1779-1848). Famous Stockholm chemist, interested in rare metals and the discoverer of cerium, zirconium, thorium, selenium and silicon. A splendid teacher with famous pupils.

laboratory, but for a long time has not worked." In 1821 Dr. Marcet [1] wrote to Berzelius, "Hatchett is taking care of his money . . . but is no longer doing anything in chemistry", but in the same year the mineral *Hatchettite* was named by the Rev. J. J. Conybeare in honour of "the eminent chemist to whom we are indebted for the most valuable contributions towards the history and analysis of this class of mineral substances" (i.e. the bituminous minerals).

Whatever his attitude to chemistry Hatchett was busy battling with ill health and after 1830 with bringing up the orphaned children of his son. Sometime after 1818 he repurchased the house Belle Vue, in Chelsea, a house built by his father in 1771 and in which Charles had spent his childhood. Here he collected a fine library and gave much time to the enjoyment of music. He had a music room with a good organ, and made a "tolerable" collection of musical instruments and music mss, many of which are now in the mss room at the British Museum. He died on the 10th of February, 1847, and was buried at St. Lawrence's church, Upton-cum-Chalvey, Buckinghamshire, near his parents and wife. Among the famous embroidered kneelers in Chelsea Old Church there is one to his memory, "Writer, Savant, Collector".

His work on the bitumens was widely quoted by later writers, such as Parkinson in his *Antedeluvian World*, vol. I (1804), letter XXII, who speaks of the "great obligations which the lovers of chemistry owe to Mr. Hatchett for his ingenious observations on the nature of bitumens . . . " and in Letter XXIII his ideas on the origin of coal are given prominence. He is quoted again by later writers on "fossil fuels" and on the origin of coal and of bituminous substances. In the world of mineralogy he was recognised by the naming of Hatchettite, and in 1877 by the American J. L. Smith who named a mineral which proved to be a columbate of uranium, *Hatchettolite*. He has a place in the Dictionary of National Biography, and a chief source for his chemical work is in the extended references in the volume produced for the (American) Journal of Chemical Education, *Discovery of the Elements*, by M. E. Weeks (U.S.A. 1945) which has been used in this summary of his work.

[1] Alexander Marcet (1770-1822). Close friend and correspondent of Berzelius. Lecturer in chemistry at Guy's Hospital, London.

THE DIARY

APRIL 26TH—1796 Set out from Hammersmith at 6 oClock in the Morning, by the Salisbury Coach. There were three other Passengers viz a Mr. Eyre of Brickworth (about 6 miles from Salisbury) an uncle of Mrs. R. Thornton's, a Mr. Grove a Clergyman and a Miss Robson a fat Milliner of Salisbury—dined at Popham Lane—and arrived at Salisbury at 8 oClock—about the 44 Mile Stone the chalk begins to appear and then continues thro' the rest of Wiltshire and the whole of Dorsetshire to the sea.

Coach	£1	5	0
Coachmen		2	0
Breakfast		2	0
Dinner		4	6
	£1	13	6

Salisbury 82 miles from London, about Stockbridge the road is hilly and again about 2 Miles before Salisbury. Went to Mr. Maton's.

WEDNESDAY, APRIL 27TH Remained with Mr. Maton at Salisbury.

THURSDAY APRIL 28TH Set out in Mr. Maton's Carriage for Woodyeat's. Arrived there at 12 oClock. Went in a Post chaise to Blandford 12 miles, met Rockett at Dr. Pulteney's. Went in Mr. R's coach with Dr. and Mrs. P. to Spetisbury.

Chaise	£0	14	0
Driver		2	0
	£0	16	0

FRIDAY APRIL 29TH Mr. Savaresi came to Spetisbury. Went to Blandford in the evening.

SATURDAY APRIL 30TH Went to Dr. Pulteney's after breakfast. Wrote to Mrs. C. H.

SUNDAY MAY 1ST After dinner went to Blandford and from thence set out with Mr. Savaresi in a Post chaise for Dorchester at ½ past 6—arrived at Dorchester by ¼ before 9—the first 8 or 9 Miles very hilly —sup'd and slept at the King's Arms—Dorchester 16 Miles from Blandford.

Chaise	18	8
Driver	2	4
Turnpikes	1	0
£1	2	0

Paid for my part 0. 11. 0

MONDAY MAY 2ND Set out at 9 oClock in the morning for Weymouth in a Post Chaise—near Dorchester is a Roman Amphitheatre of Turf very perfect. The road to Weymouth is hilly and near W. goes down to the flat on which it is built. Weymouth is 8 Miles from Dorchester—the shore at W. is flat and sandy—went on the sands to the Ferry House and passed over in the Ferry Boat to the Isle of Portland. Were landed on a stoney and sandy bank (a part of the Chessil Bank) and walked about 3 Miles before we reached the Island—The stones on this Bank are of various sizes and mixed, being composed of rounded fragments of Portland Stone, Flint and Quartz. Visited the quarries at Portland. The whole Island appears to be composed of Calcareous Grit or Sandstone which is in beds of 5 or 6 or 8 feet thick laying nearly horizontal; between these beds are strata of Black and Grey Schistose Flint varying from 1 to 5 or 6 inches or more in thickness—above the stone is a hard schistose Gritty Marle which often has land or marine fossils upon it—this Schistose Marle is commonly about 12 feet in depth and is cover'd by a small quantity of Vegetable Earth and grass.—The Portland Stone is full of shells such as Turbinites or their Nuclei. When worked or rubbed it emits a strong Bituminous smell like Lapis Smillus—it has often also between the Beds thin strata of soft brown Argillaceous Marle—when the flint is brown it often contains shells like the Portland stone, but the black or grey schistose flint does not contain any.

I also found various pieces of white petrified wood on which were small crystallisations of Quartz.—The shells do not prevail in the whole mass but appear to form bands or strata thus. Portland also affords several rare Plants particularly the Euphorbia Portlandica—the Inhabitants 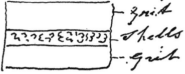 catch various kinds of fish such as Mackerel, Lobsters, Crabs and Prawns. Dined at the New Hotel in Portland.

Dinner	0	4	0
Wine		3	6
Beer			3
Servant		1	3

half 0 4 6	£0	9	0

Returned over the Ferry at 5 oClock PM and arrived again at Dorchester by 7 oClock.

Bill	0	17	9
Waiter	0	2	0
Ch. maid	0	4	0
Boots	0	2	0
Post boy	0	3	0
Chaise	0	14	0

Half £1. 1. 6	£2	3	0

TUESDAY MAY 3RD At one in the morning set out in the Exeter Coach or Spanish Mail for Exeter. Rainy morning—In the coach was a young Gunner going to Plymouth pretty much in liquor, a Mrs. Dawson wife of Sir E Pelew's gunner going to join her husband at Plymouth, a young woman going also to Plymouth and two children of Mrs. Dawson, one 9 and the other 6 years old. The coach was therefore much crowded so that I was exceedingly crippled; and on account of the Heat, Pressure and Stench from the Sailor of Gin and Tobacco, Savaresi seemed to think that he was got into a place like the Black Hole at Calcutta. As it rained the females wanted to have the Glasses up, but were stoutly opposed by Mr. S. who carried at length his point, being greatly agitated. He swore in Italian, German, French and broken English. The children were sometimes upon our knees and at other times kicked my shins. Savaresi kept his nose out at the window—by degrees we arranged ourselves

rather better—The Sailor was very sweet on the young woman—
Mrs. Dawson was a rather pretty woman about 28. Passed through
Bridport 16 Miles from Dorchester from thence went thro' Char-
mouth to Axminster in Devonshire 12 Miles where we breakfasted
at the George—proceeded to Honiton 9 Miles. Country very beautiful and all the way very hilly. From Honiton went to Exeter 16 Miles.

Coach	1	0	0
Baggage		3	0
Porter		1	0
Coachman		2	0
Breakfast		1	6
For myself	£1	7	6

WEDNESDAY MAY 4TH Exeter is nearly surrounded with hills and is
in a sort of Basin which rises in the middle. The soil is argillaceous,
tinged of a full Brick red by Oxyd of Iron and probably some
Manganese. This red colour prevails as far as Sidmouth. After
dinner went with Mr. Kingdon to Newton St Cyres to see some new
Manganese Pits lately opened. The Manganese is found at from 4 to
12 feet from the grass in a red clay. The quality of the Manganese is
not at present so good as that which was found at Upton Pynes, but
much resembles it and probably may equal it when digged deeper.—
Newton St. Cyres is nearly 4 Miles to the North West of Exeter—
Went to Upton Pynes where are the remains of the former Manganese Pits which are now nearly filled up. The Manganese was found
in Nodules immediately under the grass to the depth of 20 feet—
that at Newton is much deeper—Upton Pynes is $3\frac{1}{2}$ miles from
Exeter.—Went to the quarries in the Raddon Village in the Parish
of Thorverton. The stone is known by the name of Thorverton
Stone and is used for building and is particularly excellent to make
the bottoms of ovens. The stone is found at 4 or 6 feet from the
surface and between it and the Vegetable Earth some strata of clay
and pale grey Marle. The stone does not appear in strata but is solid
with some small transverse or vertical cracks or fissures. It is grey
and sometimes reddish with nodules of calcareous spar. Sometimes
there are small Nodules of a dark green. In certain portions the
Nodules are decomposed and have left the stone so as to give it a
cavernous or porous appearance like certain Lava's of a reddish

colour. The stone is then called by the people Honeycomb Stone. In certain varieties there are strata of a pale reddish brown compact Limestone (?) without any nodules and the whole stone effervesces with acids, often however but slightly. It breaks hard and some of the larger Nodules are said to be found to contain water. The Manganese of Newton is principally sold to the Bleachers. This stone is a variety of Toadstone.

Paid Post Boy   0   2   6
Turnpikes   9

At Newton the refuse Manganese was used to strew over the fields and Mr. Kingdon said that the crop of grass was thereby much increased, probably there is much Manganese in the red ferruginous loam which abounds in Devon, and may be one of the causes of its fertility. Also the nodules of Manganese may have formed from the red Oxyd of Manganese contained in the red loam and clay, by receiving an addition of Oxygen.

THURSDAY MAY 5TH   At 10 oClock in the morning set out for Chudleigh and Bovey—near the 5 Mile Stone the red soil changes to a pale brown sandy soil with many flints scattered about and many indications of the presence of calcareous earth. Arrived at Chudleigh 9½ Miles by 12 oClock went on to Bovey Hayfield[1] to see the Bovey Coal Pits. They are about 2 Miles beyond Chudleigh on a Heath which in that part is flat and sandy but to the west of the Pits at about 100 yards there is a bog of considerable extent where they cut turf and find decayed roots and trunks of Trees which however do not at all resemble the Bovey Coal. There is a thin sandy stratum on which ericas grow, where the coal is found, which is succeeded by a stratum of pale greyish brown clay which towards the North part of the Pit is about 6 feet in depth and is intermixed with stones chiefly quartz etc of various sizes. The Coal then appears in strata with clay interposed between them. The quality of the coal varies but is better and more solid towards the South, than the North. The leading part or direction of the strata of coal is from East to West and the dip or inclination is from North to South. The strata of coal vary in thickness, the thickest stratum is near the bottom and is from 6 to 8 feet. It is in fact composed of 4 smaller, but as the intermediate clay is very thin they are considered as one. There are

*Heathfield.

in all 17 distinct strata which from the grass to the bottom produce a Pit which is 74 feet deep. The great stratum of coal which has been mentioned has two other strata under it, but in summer time these with some others are covered with water to the depth of about 40 feet. In winter they can get at the lower strata because a greater quantity of water comes down to work the Engine. The Engine is put in motion by an Overshot wheel 24 feet in Diameter which works two leavers with rods and buckets. There is also an undershot wheel in another part which is sometimes used. They do not find coal below the lower bed or stratum, altho they have tryed to the additional depth of 32 feet; they only found strata of sand and clay and lastly quicksand with much water. In winter 12 men can raise 120 Tons of coal in a week.

The water in the Pit has a ferruginous taste and deposits some ochre. There is also on some of the coal which has been exposed to the air a Vitriolic efflorescence. The men said that some years ago a part of the Pit took fire at about 20 feet deep which they could not extinguish by water but were forced to cover it to stifle the fire. The water also in one of the Pits was warm.

Turnpikes	0	1	3
Men at Bovey	2	0
Men at the Pottery	2	6
Bill at Chudleigh	9	0
Post Boy	4	0
£0	18	9

The water which works the Engines is conveyed in Wooden Troughs. There is Heath and Sand but no boggy Turf over the Bovey Coal.

Went to the Pottery at Bovey under the direction of a Mr. Crane. The ware is the yellow or Queen's Ware. The clay which is very fine is brought from about 5 Miles from Bovey. In returning to Chudleigh we visited the Marble quarry about ¼ of a Mile from the town on the Bovey Road. The Marble is a dark grey veined with white Calc: Spar. It is fine grained, is hard, and bears a good polish. It is in strata of 5 or 6 feet thick, the direction or Lead of which is nearly from North to South and the dip or inclination is from N West to S East. Over the Marble next the grass is a thin stratum of yellowish red gravelly Marle.

FRIDAY MAY 6TH

No. 1 Bill at Exeter	£2	3	0
No. 2 ,, ,,		11	0
Bill at Chudleigh		18	9
Post to Moreton & Tavistock			
With Bill at Moreton	2	9	3
Post chaises to			
Thorverton & Bovey	1	10	6

Half £3.16.3	£7	12	6

At 11 oClock set out in a Post Chaise for Moreton Hempstead within a mile of Exeter on this side the red soil disappeared and the road becomes rough and hilly and is cut through a grey Argillaceous Schistus which separates into plates not very thin. The whole country is Mountainous and is probably composed of the same schistus. Near the 9 Mile Stone the country appears strewed with blocks of granite and the schistus no longer appears, but all the Mountains exhibit granite. This granite varies from small grained to large with crystals of white and red feldtspar sometimes 4 or 5 inches long and proportionably thick. The component parts are feldtspar quartz with a very little black mica in small particles. The quartz sometimes much predominates, at other times the feldtspar. In this granite veins of black shorl appear running East and West. The schorl is sometimes in a mass accompanied by quartz or feldtspar, at other times crystallised in prisms of various sizes which sometimes are arranged in a radiating manner. Dined at Moreton Hempstead 12 miles from Exeter. Set out for Tavistock at ½ past 4 oClock. About ¼ of a Mile from Tavistock the granite becomes in many places friable and decomposed. The schorl accompanies as before. Road very hilly and rough (NB the granite first appears near a village called Dockham on the hill called Dockham Hill). At about 6 Miles from Moreton H. on the left hand or south of the road going to Tavistock at the distance of a Mile on Dartmoor is a Tin Mine called Vytifor under the direction of a Capt. Craze to whom we had a letter from Mr. Kingdon. The main lode or Vein of this Mine runs East and West, dipping or inclining a little from South to North, and is already known to extend about ¼ of a Mile. There are considerable remains of antient channels cut down upon the lode in former times by streaming. The general country of the

Mine is a soft pale red decomposed granite or Growan. The lodes or veins vary in size from an inch to 12 or 20. The main lode has several branches.

The works were begun towards the West. The lode runs in a matrix of Quartz often accompanied by the black schorl above mentioned, also with Peach or chlorite of different tints of green and between the lode and wall of the mine generally runs a thin vein of Eisenglimmer. The same iron ore is often found in large quantities in parts of the Vein and is sold to Mr. Kingdon. The Tin is partly in small prisms of a pale brown which again are often coated by a pale brown earthy tin ore somewhat resembling Wood Tin.

The ore is sent to be smelted at about 4 or 8 (?) Miles from Tavistock. 40 men are employed in the mine. There are 8 shafts to the West and 5 to the East. The western shaft will when completed be 40 Fathoms in depth. The Engine shaft is about 21 fathoms. The Engine goes by water and has an overshot wheel. The soil about Dartmoor is very boggy in many places—near the mine is a rabbit warren which lets at £80 per ann.

As the direction of the Lodes of Vytifor have the same direction and are accompanied by the same schorl as that found at Dockham, may not the latter be a continuation of the Lode?

NB there are 3 levels in Vytifor each of 7 Fathoms.

SATURDAY MAY 7TH The preceeding night we arrived and sup'd at the Bedford Arms at Tavistock which is 20 miles from Moreton Hempstead, the road very rough the chief part over Dart Moor—granite all the way to Tavistock. On Saturday morning after Breakfast went with Mr. Curtis (to whom I had a letter from Mr. Simpson of Lime Street) to see Wheal Friendship Mine, a Copper Mine which is about 4 Miles from Tavistock on the south side of the Okehampton Road at the borders of Dart Moor. This mine was begun about 5 years ago and began to return some profit within the last year and a ½. The first stratum in blackish caple. The next is a greenish and blueish grey Killas (chlorit passing to Thon schiefer) in which the Lode or Vein is found. The Lode is accompanied by quartz. The direction is from East to West and the dip or underlay or inclination is from South to North, making a difference of 5 feet in a fathom. The known length of the Lode is about 60 fathoms. The water is drawn out by an Overshot wheel of 26 feet, which works two Levers and Rods with buckets in a shaft 28 fathoms deep from the grass. There is one other shaft. There are between 40 and 50 men employed under ground besides others with Women and Boys who are employed to dress and clean the ore. There is a stamping mill and other requisite works. The Ore is yellow or Pyritical Copper often pretty rich and sometimes coloured, accompanied by Galena and some Blende. They can raise about 40 Tons per Month which when dressed will sell at £13 per Ton. The ore is sold in Cornwall and is generally smelted in Wales.

From hence we went to view a Lode of Gossan in the neighbourhood at about 2 Miles distance in the same direction with the Lode in Huel Friendship, i.e. E to W. Afterwards went beyond the 5 Mile Stone on the Okehampton road to the south on the Heath about 1½ or 2 Miles to see Huel Jewel, a Tin mine. The direction and inclination of the Lode is the same as in Huel Friendship, the length about 100 fathoms and the depth 50 fathoms, about 40 Men are employed underground besides others above. They have a Water Engine with a wheel as in the Huel Friendship. There are 2 shafts. The country of the mine is a sort of pale grey killas which becomes ochry & red by exposure to the air. The Lode is Vitreous Tin in small particles mixed with a blackish brown caple.

The Tin is rarely crystallised and then only I have seen it in small crystals. There is a house by the mine where the Tin Ore is roasted. The operation is sometimes only done once, never oftener than twice. The floor of the furnace one length of a Brick thick with stone under it. Fuel is Pit Coal. The Engine shaft is towards the East of the Lode.

	£		
Turnpike	£0	0	6
Post boys refresh:			6
Post boy		2	0
		0	3	0
Gave at H. Friendship		1	0
	£0	4	0

Mr. Curtis dined with us on a very bad dinner of fish and tough beef steaks. The Smelting House near Tavistock belongs to a Mr. Lane, but as it was not on so large a scale and was not equal to those in Cornwall we did not go to see it.

SUNDAY MAY 8TH Set out from Tavistock at $\frac{1}{2}$ past 10 oClock the road but indifferent and hilly. On leaving Tavistock, Grey Killas or what Mr. Savaresi considers as a species of Thon Schiefer. At about 3 miles from Tavistock passed the Tamar over an old stone bridge and entered Cornwall. Here the mountains are pretty considerable, and small blocks of granite appeared scattered on the heath. Near the Bridge on each side of the River are two small mines, there is also another a little beyond on the side of Cornwall. On the Heath appear many pits sunk in the seeking for mines. After the 6 Mile Stone we did not see any killas for some time. Arrived at Callington 9 Miles from Tavistock at about 12. Near Callington are several Tin Mines but I believe not considerable. I remember that during my Tour in 1794 I visited a Mine on Kits Hill where I found great quantities of Wolfram mixed with quartz. From Callington we set out for Liskeard, the road not very hilly nor rough. It was for the most part enclosed by Hedges. Thick grey killas or schistus appeared in many places. We reached Liskeard at about 2 oClock and dined. Liskeard is but a poor built town and is 9 miles from Callington. At 3 we set out for Lostwithiel 12 Miles. The road was excellent and the country as far as the bad weather would permit us to see was in general well cultivated. The killas still seemed to prevail. At about 4 Miles from Lostwithiel we saw some granite in blocks and on the brow of the Mountain passed over some heathy ground and arrived at Lostwithiel by 6 oClock. Could not get another chaise and went on in the same towards St. Austle.

Killas in general still prevailed and in some parts the soil was very red which might be partly occasioned by the custom they have of burning the land, and partly by the decomposition of the killas which I have observed often to become pulverulent and of an Ochry red colour. Mr. S. however was not of the same opinion. (Mr. Savaresi afterwards embraced my opinion by reason of subsequent proofs) as several Mountains appeared nearby composed of this red earth; perhaps it was some sort of Loam as it sometimes had rather a sandy appearance. At about $1\frac{1}{2}$ Miles from St. Austle we crossed a Heath.

Bill at Tavistock	2	16	0
Post to Callington 9 miles	0	10	6
Driver		1	6
Post to Liskeard 9 miles		10	6

Driver		1	6
Turnpikes	0	1	0
Bill at Liskeard		4	0
Post to Lostwithiel and			
St. Austle 21 miles	1	4	6
Driver	0	4	0
Turnpikes	0	3	0
Half £2.18.3	£5	16	6

MONDAY MAY 9TH The preceeding evening I called on Mr. C.
Rashleigh and appointed to go in the morning to the Smelting
Houses for Tin. The Smelting Houses are towards the western
extremity of St. Austle and consist of two buildings, in the first one
4 Reverberatory Furnaces built of granite.

A is the opening by which they throw
in the pulverised and washed ore
which is separated by a wall or
Bridge from the part which communicates with the opening B in which the
fire is made and the fuel cast in at B.

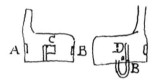

The bridge does not reach to the roof of the Furnace so that the
flame draws over the ore towards A over the top of the wall or
bridge in the middle. Sometimes the Fuel is put in at a side aperture
as at C opposite to which is at the bottom a Plate with a Hole about
one inch or rather more in Diameter which is stopped with clay,
which is broken with an Iron Rod when the ore is properly smelted
so that the melted Tin may run into a trough of granite Moor Stone
E from whence it is ladled into a large iron Bason and from thence
into granite Moulds thinly coated with clay so as to form blocks
which are again melted and cast into others of greater thickness
which weigh [1]. The scoria are stampd & washed and the tin is
melted with the second blocks. The fuel is Welsh coal. They smelt
in each furnace 700 Cwt[2] of the Ore at each time which requires
about 6 hours. The ore used in the Furnaces is from Mines and has
been repeatedly roasted and washed.

The other House is called the Blowing House. The ore smelted
there is principally or rather entirely the Stream or Shoad Tin. This

[1] blank in MS.
[2] this should read 7 Cwt.

is reduced also under a Stamping Mill and washed. It never is roasted but when by accident it contains some Pyrites which is seldom. The Furnace is 9 feet high and is built of granite with a long inclined chimney of about 20 fathoms in length which terminates at a distance in a circular building which receives the Tin accidentally raised by the Heat. The internal form of the Furnace is that of a double cone. There is an aperture A in the upper part into which the ore is cast with a certain proportion of charcoal about double in bulk. At the bottom is a hole B out at which the melted Tin flows into a Trough like in the others. The tin is ladled into an Iron Bason and a piece of oak charcoal about half burned is put into it when nearly full which occasions an ebullition and facilitates the separation of the dross which is skimmed off and melted again. The Furnace is heated with two bellows worked by a water wheel. This Tin is the fine grain Tin which is better than that of the Reverberating Furnaces. The Blast Furnace will make about 10 Blocks to 5 of one of the Reverberating Furnaces. N.B. the Tin in the Blast House is only once smelted. At about a Mile from St. Austle is another Blast Furnace which is higher than that at St. Austle and instead of Bellows has Cylinders as in certain of the Iron Founderies.

Went with Mr. C and Mr. Jonathn Rashleigh to see Charles Town built by the former. The Town, the Pier of granite and a considerable Wet Dock which at High Water has a depth of water 15 feet, with Rope Walk, Store Houses & Fish Cellars including the improved Lands about, has been done upon the sole plan and at the sole expence of Mr. C. Rashleigh upon his own estate.—A wonderful work for a private Gentleman. The whole has been begun about 3 years. Dined with Mr. C. Rashleigh—after dinner went with him to see a Mine to the SE of St. Austle about $\frac{1}{4}$ of a mile from the town called Huel Change. There is an excellent water engine the wheel of which is 36 feet which works horizontal rods 140 fathoms in length. The depth of the mine at present is 30 Fathoms. The country is grey killas and the ore raised is Vitreous Copper with black pulverulent Do. and some red Copper. This mine seems to promise well to the proprietors—it is under the direction of a Capt. Gilbert. N.B. at Mr. C. Rashleigh's new quay great quantities of the china stone or decomposed granite from St. Stephens about 5 Miles north of St. Austle were laying to be shipped for Liverpool or to be sent to Worcestershire and Staffordshire for the Porcelain Ware. N.B. Mr. Hennah told us that in the mines on the Southern Coast of Cornwall the Lodes dipped or inclined to the North but on the Northern Coast to the South.—this is not true—the dip of the Lode in Huel Change is to the North at the rate of 6 feet in the fathom.— Mr. C. Rashleigh afterwards sent me by Capt. Gilbert a fine specimen of the Vitreous Copper Ore from Huel Change.

In the Blast Furnace I noticed that the melted Tin in the Stone Trough before the Furnace was always kept covered with charcoal to prevent the Oxydation of the Metal. In the Blast Furnace they do not smelt more than 2 Cwt of Tin at one time. In the Blast Furnace as well as in the Reverberating Furnace they get more than the half of Tin from any quantity of the Ore e.g. from 600 of Ore, about 350 of Tin.

TUESDAY MAY 10TH   Went in the morning to see the collection of Mr. Hennah a clergyman in St. Austle. It was chiefly remarkable for fine wood Tin. I have for the first time seen Schiefer Spar crystallised in plates placed edgewise from Polgooth Mine, also compact Schiefer Spar coated on each side with chlorit or Peach containing small Prisms of Tin—Schiefer Spar hitherto has been supposed peculiar to Saxony.

We then set out for Truro and at about two Miles from St. Austle a little to the south of the road we stopped to see the celebrated Mine of Polgooth. This Mine has been worked by the present Adventurers about 12 years but the commencement of it is very antient. It is the largest and one of the most productive Tin Mines in Europe and probably in the World. The Main Lode which is about 6 feet thick runs from East to West and dips to the North at about 6 feet in a fathom. The length is not exactly known but is very great as it has afforded Tin during the complete length of a Mile— towards the East the Lode divides into 2 Branches. There is another Lode or Vein which cuts the former nearly at a right angle and consequently runs North and South. The dip or inclination of this is to the East. This Lode was very productive for a considerable time but is not so at present. In following the Lode thro' the usual country which is a greyish killas they came to a cross course of Elvan Stone 46 feet thick which drove the other part of the Lode about 15 feet out of the direct line.—I believe it was in this Lode that the Schiefer Spar was found and Capt. Phillips informed me that after this was found the Lode afforded very little ore. In this mine are about 50 shafts 26 of which are in use, with as many horizontal wheels or whims. There are 36 Stamping Mills with the necessary apparatus. There is a furnace for roasting the ore after it has been repeatedly stamped and washed, after it has been roasted it is washed once and then smelted at St. Austle in the Reverberating Furnaces. The depth of the Engine shaft is 123 Fathoms. 700 men etc. are employed in and upon the mine. There is a capital steam engine erected by Boulton and Watts, which at each stroke draws up a column of water 30 feet height and 15 inches diameter. There is also an excellent Water Engine with an Overshot wheel 36 feet diameter and 6 feet wide.

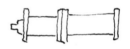

The axis is inclosed in a hollow one of cast Iron with Iron Axes and Arms which turn in collars of Brass. This wheel works two Bobs which act on two perpendicular Rods one of 20 the other of 40 Fathoms. There is also a Pump to draw off the superabundant water under the wheel in winter. The Ore seldom or never is found crystallized but is disseminated in general thro' a matrix of quartz accompanied by Peach or Chlorit and sometimes with a reddish Iron Ochre and small detached

portions of yellow Copper Pyrites. As the matrix is so hard the ore is generally blown with powder. The ore altho' not beautiful is commonly very rich and is generally pale grey or according to the quantity of Tin sometimes greyish brown. When a thin stratum of Mundic or Pyrites is found in the fissures of the Lode it is regarded as a certain sign of the richness of that part. Captn Phillips informed me that upon an average they raised ore to the value of £2800 per month but Mr. Hennah said that the Monthly expenses were £2600 and after paying this they cleared about £600 per Month, so that the amount in this case would be £3200 per month.

I got some compact Schiefer Spar from Captn Phillips and also saw some Calc: Spar into which the former passed by certain Gradations. The road all the way from St. Austle to Truro is good and not very hilly. Killas of a pale grey or grey appeared in all the places where the Mountains were cut through to make the road. Arrived at Truro at ¼ past 3 oClock, went to the Kings Head and dined. St. Austle is a tolerable town but Truro is a very neat well built Town well situated but not large.

Polgooth (addition) when I visited this Mine in 1794 they had raised some ore which was soft and friable it consisted of small grains of Tin, Mundic and chlorit loosely cohering, so that it could easily be crumbled between the fingers.—

Bill at St. Austle	1	3	6
Given at Polgooth	0	4	0
Post to Truro	0	18	0
Boy	0	2	0
	£2	7	6

Half £1 13 9
Pd for Mins.
At Truro   15 0

1 18 9

All the country from St. Austle to Truro is well cultivated.

Bill at Truro	£0	11	4
Ch. maid	0	2	0
Waiter	0	2	2
Boots	0	0	6
Half 0 8 0	£0	16	0

WEDNESDAY MAY 11TH On Wednesday morning at 10 oClock set out from Truro—at 1½ mile from the Town is the Smelting House belonging to Mr. Daniel. This Smelting House contains 10 Reverbtg Furnaces on the same principle as those at St. Austle. About 20 men are employed. I found however that I was misinformed at St. Austle for the ore is not as they said smelted without a Flux. On the contrary a certain measure of Culm Coal (which comes from Wales) is added to the ore so as to be in proportion to it as one eighth. The fuel as at St. Austle is Welsh Pit coal. The Furnaces are about 6 feet high, the internal capacity 3 ft and a ½ by 7 feet long and about 9 inches deep where the Metal is contained. The Ash hole is nearly 2 feet high by about 12 inches in width. The chimney is 40 feet high and the internal aperture one foot and a $\frac{1}{2}$. Little or no Tin is formed in these chimneys which is the reverse in the Blast Furnace. They smelt 600 Cwt of the ore every 6 hours which afford nearly 350 of Tin. One Block of Tin weighs about 320 lb and upon the average at present is worth about £12 12 0.

At about $4\frac{1}{2}$ miles from Truro are the celebrated Stream Works at Carnan. These have been worked by the present company 12 years but many circumstances prove that they have been worked in times of remote Antiquity. The present Workmen have found Oaken Shovels and a Pick Ax of Stags Horn which latter is in the possession of Mr. Fox at Falmouth. It is however remarkable that this stream work when undertaken by the present company was coverd with the sea (as the Captn informed us) when they began the work they sunk a shaft 4 fathoms deep and (when an embarkment was made to confine the water in a certain channel) the rest of the water was drawn out by a Water Engine which discharged about 1000 gallons in a minute and which now works two rods in two cylinders in a shaft 8 fathoms in depth.

The present stream works are about $\frac{3}{4}$ of a mile long by nearly 300 yards wide. 190 Men and Boys are employed in these works.

A thin stratum of sand covers these works after which about 30 feet of a black soft clay occurs; immediately under the clay the Tin Ore is found for the most part like pebbles rounded by attrition of various sizes in part mixed with the clay. Under the Tin is the rock—probably granite. Wood tin is sometimes (but rarely) found with it, and also some gold, generally in small particles. A great quantity of Shells appear in the clay in a very recent state and in the stream works at Porth near St. Austle Mr. Greville found a quantity of Hazle Nuts in a stratum of Vegetable Earth at the depth of [1] but no vestige of wood. In the last 12 years this Stream Work (Carnon) has yielded about £25000 and the present Month will afford about £700. Mr. Fox of Falmouth with Mr. Tremaine and some others are the proprietors. The two former with Mr. Rashleigh are the principal proprietors of Polgooth. The work was begun towards the North and now goes on towards the South. They advance about $1\frac{1}{2}$ feet in one day in the whole of the work.

There is here as at Porth a curious machine to transport the clay from the part which is worked.

* blank in MS.

There are 4 pairs of wheels worked by ropes moved by a double water wheel overshot so that 2 pairs with the box to contain the clay are always in the Work and 2 pair out.

A   the water wheel
B   the Axes & wheels
C   an endless rope
D   Pulleys

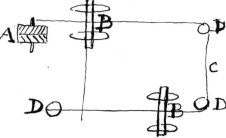

The elevated parts are towards Gwennap and the North and the river which flows into the sea by the works is said to contain much copper. In going from the Stream Works at about ½ a mile is a small Iron Foundry which we did not stop to see. Killas seems to prevail all the way from Truro to Falmouth at least as far as could be observed. The Coast also of the land near Falmouth near Pendennis Castle is pale green or greenish grey killas with white quartz interposed between the lamellae. The country in general is fertile and well cultivated between Truro and Falmouth. Near Penryn it is hilly. Arrived at Falmouth by ½ pst 2 oClock. No room to dine in but the Coffee Room and obliged to sleep in a house in the neighbourhood.

	£	s	d
Post to Falmouth 12 miles	£0	14	0
Dinner	0	2	6
Turnpikes	0	1	0
Hostler at Truro	0	0	6
half £0 9 0	0	18	0
Bill at Falmouth	0	10	6
Ch: maid	0	2	0
For waiting	0	2	6
Boots	0	1	0
half £0 8 0	£0	16	0

THURSDAY MAY 12TH In the morning at 7 oClock set out for Helstone 12 miles—passed again thro' Penryn—the country in general from Falmouth to Helstone is open, the road very good, but in some parts rather hilly, in many places well cultivated and in some it consists of Heath. From Penryn to Helstone granite appears in Blocks nearly all the way.

Post to Helstone 12 miles	£0 14	0
Dinner	0 2	0
half £0 8 0	£0 16	0

Breakfasted at the Angel Inn at Helstone—set out at $\frac{1}{2}$ past 10 for the Lizard. The country at first well cultivated but at about 2 miles fr H. it was in general flat, open and for a great part consisted of Heath. Granite at first appeared at about 2 Miles from Helstone. Large Blocks of pure white fat quartz were seen in great abundances and were used to make walls etc. Thon Schiefer then appeared and at about 8 miles from the Lizard or 2 Miles on the Helstone side of Mullion the Serpentine was first seen as a material for Walls etc. Some portions of it also began to appear in the road above the ground, the quantity gradually seemed to increase. From Mullion we took a Guide as the Post Boy did not know the road, and went to see the Soapy Rocks as they are called. The first one called Daroose and one inland at about $\frac{3}{4}$ Mile from the sea and 3 Miles from the Lizard. The Serpentine is in strata nearly horizontal about 5 feet thick, it is blackish green or brown and also with red veins, the fracture is Earthy and the surfaces of the pieces in the fissures coated with a dark shining sometimes striated green indurated Steatites like a coating of enamel.—Between the Serpentine is found an earthy steatitical matter with vestiges of Schiller Spar which is often found in the complete state in larger or smaller particles in the Serpentine with red veins. The second Soapy Rock is called Gewgreese and is about $4\frac{1}{2}$ Miles from the former in a cove by the sea shore more to the south it is like the former in respect to the Serpentine but is now worked (which the former is not) and between the strata of Serpentine contains fine Steatites marbled with white, purple, yellow and grey—this is sent to the Potteries of Porcelain in Worcestershire and Staffordshire. N.B. Mr. Savaresi as well as myself thinks there is a gradation from the Thon Schiefer to the Serpentine. In other places I also found a filamentose Talcy substance which was a pale green and appeared to be a passage of Talc into Amianthus—the Serpentine is in the fissures coated with a shining dark green indurated Steatites which in some parts becomes striated and approaches in some measure to the dark green Asbestos.

The Serpentine is not used altho it might be turned into Vessels etc as at Zöbliz in Saxony. At the Lizard there are extensive waste lands which are of good soil as appears from some parts which are cultivated. These ought not to be neglected.

FRIDAY MAY 13TH Set out from Helstone at 10 oClock in the morning towards Penzance, the road very good. The country well cultivated and apparently fertile. At about 5 miles from Helstone are some Tin Mines which are not worked at present. Passed thro Marazion and St. Michaels Mount, arrived at Penzance 13 Miles from Helstone at ½ past 11 oClock. Penzance is a pretty large Town finely situated on a declivity. Country about it is fine and air very mild. Went to see the Wherry Mine called Huel Wherry, which is about ¼ of a Mile from the Town on the South side.

The shaft of the mine is in the sea at about 70 fathoms distance from the House which contains the Steam Engine, but the old shaft was at the distance of 114 fathoms. The Works were nearly destroyed and the mine filled by the sea during the great storm in January 1796. The old shaft has been therefore given up and the present one began. The latter is already made to the depth of 4 fathoms and when completed will be 24 fathoms after which they must drive to about 12 fathoms more before they begin to cut the Vein or Lode. The old shaft was 20 fathoms and the additional depth of the present shaft is owing to the dip or inclination of the Lode to the North or towards the shore next the Town. The dip is 6 feet in one fathom—the direction of the Lode is West by South 2 points and East by North. The country is a blue killas and the Lode which is 10 fathoms wide is formed of the Vitreous Tin interspersed in an Elvan Stone (a sort of hard yellowish white or pale grey Saxum Metalliferum) which contains Feldtspar, Quartz and Peach or chlorit. These substances more or less predominate and form varieties in the Lode. Some yellow Copper Ore in small quantities also occurs in the Vein. This ore is so rich that a Barrow full is sold at £1. 4. 0—few men are employed at present but 80 men were employed before the Mine was injured by the abovementioned storm. The new shaft at Spring tides is left dry, but in general is covered with water which at high water is about 4 fathoms in depth. In the former shaft the sea water used to insinuate itself into the Mine altho the superincumbent Body of Earth was 4 fathoms in thickness. There is a wooden platform which is supported by long posts which reaches from the Engine House to the shaft. The Engine worked by Steam and is on Hornblower's principle with two cylinders, one of which receives the superabundant steam of the other, and conducts it into a condensing vessel. The Steam Engine works a horizontal rod which at the end over the shaft moves a Bob with a Rod and Bucket.

Near the Pier are some Rocks which are Killas or chlorit schiefer at bottom on which is a harder and coarser Modification of it which rather breaks into blocks of a pale grey, than into flakes.

Bill at Helstone	£1	9	2
Ch: maid	0	2	4
For waiting	0	1	6
Boots	0	1	0
Gave when at the Lizard	0	3	0
Gave man at the Soapy Rocks	0	1	0
Post to Penzance 13 M	0	15	2
Driver for 2 Days	0	5	10
Gave at the Wherry Mine	0	2	0
half £1 10 6	£3	1	0

Dined and slept at the Ship and Castle at Penzance; a very good Inn. The country round Penzance is uncommonly beautiful and fertile. The wheat is in plenty and the Sea Air does not appear to injure Vegetation.

SATURDAY MAY 14TH   Set out for St. Ives at ½ past 9 in the morning; when we had gone about 5 Miles the appearance of the country began to be changed, the fertile appearance declined and the country became more barren and was covered with blocks of granite, appearance of excavations were seen everywhere and remains of mines which had been abandoned. These increased as we approached St. Ives. We arrived at St. Ives by 12 oClock—it is a filthy town. To the East of the Town are some Rocks on the shore which in their upper Strata consist of Schorl intimately mixed with Quartz forming what in Cornwall is called Iron Stone, but from some parts in which the schorl was distinct I was able to ascertain the composition; this Rock by gradations and by the accession of chlorit passes into Chlorit Schiefer or greenish killas which appears to be the basis of the Rock, or the substance which forms the lowest stratum. Shaft for Copper in these Rocks 4 fathoms. Not worked. In this are veins of Quartz or Petro Silex in some parts also more or less penetrated by chlorit. St. Ives by the road we went is 9 miles from Penzance, at ½ past one PM set out for Camborne, the Road hilly and round by the coast of the Bay. Round St. Ives are several Tin Mines but none of considerable consequence. At the distance of 3 Miles we arrived at the Hayle which is a sand only to be crossed when the tide is out, being at other times Quick; we went over it about 1½ miles to the Copper house or the Smelting Furnaces for the Copper Ore brought from the Camborne and Gwennap Mines. It consists of several Buildings beside Houses inhabited by the People employed. Instead of Brick these are chiefly built with Square Masses of the Scoria which for that purpose is cast into Moulds as it comes out of the Furnaces. All the Furnaces used are Reverberators somewhat resembling those used for Tin at St. Austle but larger, the internal capacity of the first Roasting Furnaces being for the Ore about 18 feet long by 14 and the height varying according to the Dome from 2 to 4 feet. In these they roast at one time about 3 Tons and ½ of the Picked Ore reduced to small pieces, but that which has been stamped under the Mills is not roasted but is mixed with that which has undergone the operation and is immediately smelted—after the ore has been roasted for 12 hours it is removed into one which is smaller and which has a hopper which holds the quantity and by means of a slider with an handle B it is admitted by little into the Furnace without which precaution there would be danger of an explosion. They certainly leave it too long so as to imbibe moisture. In this second Furnace the roasted ore is melted and then tapped or let out by a trough from a hole in the side towards the bottom of the Furnace into a Tub of Wood sunk into a Pit full of water by which it is reduced into small grains. This granulated Matt is then roasted in a third Furnace and is afterwards removed to a fourth Furnace in which it is roasted and at length melted into pigs of black copper in the course of 24 hours. This operation is repeated in a 5th Furnace as many times as may be required to obtain coarse copper which is then run into moulds so as to form square blocks. The coarse copper is then removed to a sixth or Refining Furnace in which it is roasted and melted 3 times 12 hours each time. The third time produces the fine copper which is ladled into square moulds of cast iron coated with clay. The moulds contain 2 or 3 thick flat cakes of copper. This is done by only at first pouring in the quantity required to form the first cake which is suffered to cool in some degree the rest is then added so as to form the second and so on. The flux is probably Lime Stone of which great quantities were lying about. Each of the Square Cakes of Copper weigh about 150 lb. When they are full of work they employ about 150 Men with 26 Furnaces and make about 12 Tons of Copper per week. The Refining Furnace holds 3200 lb of Metal. When we saw them they were casting round cakes to flatten into copper bottoms for boiling vessels. The ladles which they used held each 25 lb and were coated with clay. The Melted Copper in the Refining Furnace is covered with charcoal and towards the end of the operation they put in a wooden pole or small trunk of a Tree which produces an ebulition and contributes to purify the metal which is repeatedly taken out in a small ladle to be assayed by hammering and by the fracture. The fuel used in the Furnaces is Welsh Pit coal and the Furnaces have the same sort of Bridge in the interior as those at St. Austle, so that only the flame plays over the copper as Pit coal would be highly detrimental was it to come into contact with the copper. All the operations take up nearly 2 weeks. The Men suffer much in Health. Mr. Savaresi thinks it would be better if the ore was melted at once into a Matt without any previous roasting and that this Matt should be roasted repeatedly and then smelted to obtain the metal.

Arrived at Camborne by ½ past 5 oClock—went to the Prince George.

Bill at Penzance	£0	14	7
Bill at St. Ives	0	5	6
Post to St. Ives 9 M ⎫			
Camborne 11 M ⎰	1	3	4
Driver	0	3	0

Gave at Copper House		0	3	6	
Turnpike		0	0	6	

half £1. 5. 0		£2	10	5

SUNDAY MAY 15TH   The preceeding evening I went to the compting house at Cooks Kitchen and delivered Sr Frs. Basset's[1] Letter to Mr. Kevill of Trevenson. This morning Capt Andrew Vivian[2] and Capt Josh Vivian called to conduct us to the Mines of Camborne and Illogan.

The mines are in a line 10 points to North of East and the same South of West at the foot of a range of hills on the extreme Eastern point of which stands the remains of Cairnbree Castle. These hills follow the same direction with the Lode or Vice Versa. The Lode is on the Northern side of these hills. In going from the West or from Camborne the first Mine is Huel Gons, a copper Mine which has been worked by the present set or Society for Copper about 20 years but was worked long before for Tin which lay on the back of the Copper Lode. This mine is 150 fathoms deep in the Engine shaft— there are 3 other shafts. There is one Steam Engine on Boulton's principle and 2 water wheels, 36 feet in diameter one above ground and the other in the Mine. There are 11 Levels in the whole depth of the Mine. 150 Men and Boys are employed above and under-ground. The country is grey killas 30 fathoms from the surface to the Lode or 10 fathoms under the Adit which consequently must be 20 fathoms deep from the surface. N.B. this Adit communicates through all the Camborne Mines.

The ore is the yellow copper in a matrix of Quartz which sometimes contains some chlorit and killas. The Lode is from 10 to 12 feet wide. sometimes only one foot. There are 4 Stamping Mills now in use. They now raise about 80 or 100 Tons per Month of ore worth £9

[1] One of the Basset family of Tehidy, a family interested in many mines in the Illogan and Camborne areas, notably in Dolcoath. The family fortunes began with the discovery of the immensely rich Trevenson mine in the course of driving Pool Adit in the 1740's. Sir Francis Basset took the title of Lord de Dunstanville.
[2] Captain Andrew Vivian known in Camborne as "Old Capun Andrew". He was associated with his cousin Richard Trevithick the engineer, and on December 28th 1801 it was he who steered Trevithick's "road carriage" on its trial journey towards Tehidy House. In London, March 6 1802, he signed, on behalf of himself and Trevithick, the Letters Patent Specification for their joint patent "Steam Engine, improvement in the construction thereof and Application thereof for drawing Carriages." He was widely interested in mines in Cornwall.

per Ton. I went down this Mine in 1794 with the Capt Andrew Vivian. The Mine was then 140 fathoms deep and was poor but lately at the additional depth of 10 fathoms they have discovered the Lode very large and very rich.

DOLCOATH IN CAMBORNE PARISH

Dolcoath is a Copper Mine on the same line to the East of Huel Gons—the Eastern part of this Mine was called Bullen Garden but when Dolcoath was discovered the whole assumed the latter name. This Mine was very productive and the ore was chiefly as at Huel Gons. Cobalt was also found occasionally with the Copper Ore to the amount of several Tons. The country is killas and granite. The Lode as at Huel Gons—the depth of the Engine shaft 174 fathoms—it has a cross course on the East & West by which the water is kept from the other Mines in the East and West and when it rises to a level with the Adit it is carried off thereby.

COOKS KITCHEN IN ILLOGAN PARISH

This is one of the most remarkable Mines for copper perhaps in the world. This mine is to the East of Dolcoath. The depth of the Steam Engine shaft is 145 fathoms from the surface and is on the South or Dunkins Lode. The Steam Engine is one of Boulton's with a 36 inch Cylinder. The Water Engine shaft is on the Great or North Lode and is 110 fathoms deep. There are three overshot wheels well and simply made, two of which are above ground viz one of 42 feet diameter and the second of 48 feet. The third is 54 feet diameter and is underground. The Steam Engine draws from the bottom of the Mine and the Water Engines deliver the water to the Adit which is at the depth of 25 fathoms from the surface. 340 Men and Boys are employed in all—170 Men are underground. Dunkins Lode is laid open 160 fathoms in length under the surface. The Great Lode is also laid open 160 fathoms at the depth of 110 fathoms. Toays Lode is laid open 40 to 50 fathoms—all the work is discharged through 4 shafts. The Ore is chiefly the Vitreous Copper called by them Grey Ore mixed sometimes with some black pulverulent Ore—also with the yellow ore in small quantities—these are mixed with quartz and gossan, also with Flookan coloured with the red Oxyd of Iron which red colour is a sure and good sign of the presence of the Grey Ore. This mine produces the fine crystallized copper on the yellow blistered ore or on the black pulverulent Ore—when the crystallized ore fails the compact generally becomes poor. The country in Dunkins Lode to 17 fathoms is granite then 20 fathoms of grey killas. The North Wall in this Lode was at first killas and the South Wall granite, now sometimes one is granite and the other becomes killas and sometimes both are killas or both granite. The Great Lode has also sometimes granite but all the other Lodes have killas for their walls. From 300 to 350 tons per Month have been raised at an average of £8 per Ton but some is worth £30. In the last 10 years a clear profit has been produced of £100,000 after the dues to the Lord of 1/6 and the Expences of the Mine have been deducted—

1/6 dues to Sr F Basset for 1795   £5323
        multiply by   6

                        £31938

Expences of the Mine is about £14000 per Ann.
Sir F.B. has 1/8 as an Adventurer

    5323   31938
   14000   19323

  £19323   £12615 profit for year 1795
   1/8 about   £1300
   1/6   5323

     £6623 to Sr F.B.

The Basset Family have from the Camborne Mines cleared about £300,000 or more.

COOKS KITCHEN MINE

Dunkins Lode dips about		16 inches in a Fathom	South
Toays Lode	do	16 do	North
Great Lode	do	16 do	South
Dunstones Lode	do	6 do	South
Engine Lode	do	2 feet	North
Sawpit Lode	do	2 feet	North
Bree Lode	do	18 inches	South

TIN CROFT IN ILLOGAN PARISH

Tin Croft is the last or extreme Eastern Mine of this range and the Engine House is about 80 fathoms from that of Cooks Kitchen. The present workings is on the same Lode as the one called Dunkins Lode. The Steam Engine is on Hornblower's Principle.

There are 6 shafts with the Engine shaft—the latter is 81 fathoms from the surface—200 Men are employed, 140 of whom are underground. The Ore is the same as at Cooks Kitchen and Muriate? and

South

Dunkins Lode from 4 to 10 feet wide

30 Fath

Toay's Lode abt 2 feet

20 Fath

Great Load from 10 to 30 feet wide

10 Fath

Dunstones Load about 18 inches wide

16 Fath

Engine Lode from 1 to 3 feet wide

15 Fath

Saw Pit Lode from 6 inches to 18 inches

20 Fath

Bue Lode from 4 feet to 20 feet wide

Arseniate of copper are also found, but now seldom. All other circumstances are as in Cooks Kitchen. This range of mines extend about 1 & ½ miles. N.B. there are in the neighbourhood several other mines.

It is worthy of notice that the red Oxyd of Iron which colours the Lodes in Cooks Kitchen does not appear in Huel Gons neither is the grey or Vitreous copper of Cooks Kitchen found in Huel Gons but only the yellow Copper Ore. I am inclined to suspect that as the yellow copper consists of copper, iron and sulphur, and the Vitreous Ore only of copper and sulphur, that in Cooks Kitchen the chief part of the Iron has been Oxydated and has remained mixed with the Matrix and in the Huel Gons the Iron has entered as a constituent part of the Ore? from the hardness etc of the Grey Ore from Cooks Kitchen Mr. Savaresi thinks that it is not a perfect Vitreous copper but that it is rather a modification between it and the Grey Ore or Fahlerz and may contain silver? In Huel Gons great quantities of quartz crystallized has been found with cavities left by large cubes (perhaps of fluor) filled with a friable yellow copper ore. Fluor is found in Huel Gons but has not been seen in crystals.

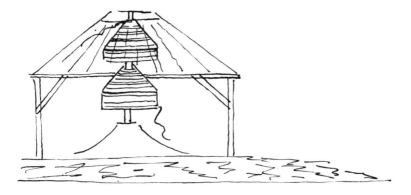

Form of the whims at Cooks Kitchen by which the weight of a great length of Rope in a deep shaft is balanced.

MONDAY MAY 16TH   Set out at 12 oClock for St. Agnes abt 10 Miles from Camborne—passed thro Redruth, arrived at St. Agnes by 3 oClock PM. The Town is but poorly built, near the Northern Coast —the road to it was very bad being over the North Downs amongst the Mines of that District. Between the town of St. Agnes and the sea the chief part in Number and in Value of the Mines are situated— these are for the most part Tin Mines, altho Mr. Williams of Scorrier said that they raised good yellow copper ore which they treated badly as they stamped the large as well as the small fragments. The country of the Mines at St. Agnes is a pale bluish grey killas or Chlorit Schiefer. The most celebrated Tin Mine is called Seal Hole— the Engine shaft is 90 fathoms deep. The Steam Engine is one of Boultons. There are many veins or Lodes; the principal Lode is called Poll Lode and dips a few points to South but the other Lodes dip to North faster or with a greater degree of inclination. The Lodes run nearly East and West. There are near 400 Men employed in this mine. This Mine affords Tin and Copper but principally the former. The ore is the Vitreous Tin accompanied by Killas, Caple (which seems to be a compound of Petro Silex with more or less blackish Schistus or Argill) and Quartz. This mine yields the killas with Veins of Tin.

Near the Town is the Mine called Huel Rock which affords the Sulphurated Tin, but it is no longer worked nor can anyone at present descend into the Mine. As it was late we could not see any thing more, nor obtain further information from Capt. Seymour the chief in the office, to whom we had a letter from Capt. A. Vivian. N.B. the Adventurers in Seal Hole last quarter divided £4000.

Dealers in Minerals at St. Agnes

Mr. Philips
Mr. Fras. Newton, Watchmaker
Mr. Thos Roberts, Hair Dresser

Returned to Redruth to Pearce's Hotel where we slept.

Expences at Camborne	£1	2	0
Do at St. Agnes	0	5	0
half £0 13 6	1	7	0
Pd at St. Agnes for Minerals	£4	3	0
do at Redruth	3	3	0
do at Truro	1	5	6
do at Penryn	0	12	0
	£9	3	6

TUESDAY MAY 17TH   After Breakfast we went to Mr. Williams of Scorrier House[1] the Principal Agent for the North Down and Gwenap Mines. These Mines are about 1 & ½ Miles Eastward of Redruth—the North Downs immediately to the North and those of Gwenap about 1 & ½ Miles to the South. One Adit runs through all these Mines and is nearly 10 Miles in length.

The North Downs Consolidated Mines occupy an extent of ground about 2 miles long and one mile in breadth. They are at present 9 in number viz—(for Copper principally).

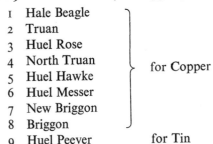

1	Hale Beagle	
2	Truan	
3	Huel Rose	
4	North Truan	for Copper
5	Huel Hawke	
6	Huel Messer	
7	New Briggon	
8	Briggon	
9	Huel Peever	for Tin

The general country of these Mines is a very clayey or loose greyish white killas. Sometimes a floor or stratum of dark blue killas approaching to Argills Schistus has been found (particularly in Briggon) which for the depth it lasts (3 or 4 fathom) renders the ore poor in quality and quantity. Some Tin is occasionally found with the copper and also a little copper with the Tin at Huel Peever. The Tin is in caple, the copper in killas. The Ore of these mines is principally the yellow copper, the best of which is at New Briggon. This is worth about £12 pr Ton the other from £8 to 9 or 10. Some of the loose black pulverulent ore is also found with the yellow Ore at Hale Beagle. There are above 40 Lodes or Veins which generally have their direction about 2 points to North of East and the same to North of West so that the direction may be considered as East and West. The dip or inclination of the Copper Lodes is generally to the North but the Tin Lodes dip to the South. The Lodes are

[1] Scorrier House, the home of John Williams was said by C. S. Gilbert to "contain the most valuable variety of mineral specimens of any house in Europe". It was visited by many eminent men and must have been irresistible to Hatchett. The Williams family from 1715 had been active in mining and about 1748 initiated the great County Adit. Scorrier House was built by the John to whom Hatchett had introductions. The family became prominent in copper smelting in Wales.

seldom larger than 3 or 4 feet and sometimes only 3, 2 or one inch. Hale Beagle is abt 35 fathoms deep and is 20 fathoms above the Adit which must in that place be therefore 55 fathoms.

Dined with Mr. Williams—after dinner went to see the Gwenap Mines. These Mines are numerous and of these we visited Huel Gorland (perhaps Garland) which affords a rich black pulverulent Copper Ore very rare in copper Mines in general. This ore is accompanied by quartz, green fluor and some Fluken or a loose clayey sort of Lithomarga—perhaps this may contain some silver? Huel Jewel is also a rich Mine which affords yellow red and black Ore. Poldice has afforded both Tin and Copper—at present it is only worked in part on account of the quantity of water. It is an old and valuable Mine. I found Wolfram and a quantity of a variety of the Bunt Kupfererz.

Huel Unity is reckoned one of the best Mines and it yields black copper ore as well as a great quantity of the Grey Ore like that of Cooks Kitchen. Mr. Williams even considers it as part of the same Lode. The country of these mines is Growan or Granite—the Lodes are abt 3 or 4 feet wide.

	£	s	d
Expences at Redruth	£0	14	0
Chaise for 2 Days	1	13	0
Driver	0	4	0
half £1 5 6	£2	11	0

In the evening went to Truro 8 miles from Redruth.

WEDNESDAY MAY 18TH   Set out at 2 oClock from Truro and arrived at the Indian Queen 12 miles near St. Columb by 4 oClock, the road good but rather hilly. Killas in many places. The country on this side of Truro well cultivated and for the most part open. Near St. Columb are some stream works but not very considerable—went to Bodmin 11 miles. Dined at the White Hart. The country about Bodmin and from St. Columb very open and part heath—road very good. At seven oClock set out for Launceston 21 miles, road very hilly at first and afterwards in many places. Did not get to Launceston till near 12 oClock PM. The country about Launceston is very hilly and pretty well coverd with wood in many places.

	£	s	d
Bill at Truro etc & chaise	£1	7	6
do Bodmin & do	1	1	10

do Launceston do	1 16 0
do Okehampton & do	1 10 4
Chaise to Torrington etc	1 7 7

| half £3 11 6 | £7 3 3 |

THURSDAY MAY 19TH Set out at 6 oClock AM for Oakhampton 20 M the road good—killas & schistus appeared in some parts, and on the Heath near Oakhampton masses of chert veined with quartz in part crystallized were seen. Arrived at Oakhampton by 10 oClock, breakfasted at the White Horse. Set out at 11 oClock for Torrington 20 miles road very hilly and bad. Near Oakhampton found some pieces of grey Porphyry Schiefer on the road—and some Miles beyond observe pale grey Micaceous Argills Grit. Arrived at Torrington (a borough Town but not represented) by 3 oClock. T is a tolerable town. The country is Mountainous about it but fine and well cultivated. Torrington is built on the side of the Summit of a Hill—went to the Globe Inn. The only chaise which was kept in the Town was engaged and we were obliged to sleep at Torrington— near the town I observed the same red loamy soil which I had noticed about Exeter.

FRIDAY MAY 20TH Sent for a chaise from Barnstaple and set out at ½ past 9 or 10 oClock road very rough and hilly—at about ½ way between Torrington and Barnstaple one of the hind wheels of the chaise flew off and had not the wheel on the other side slipd into a ditch we must have been overturned. We arrived at Barnstaple at abt 12 oClock. B is 11 Miles from Torrington. It is a considerable town beautifully situate in a plain and a branch of the sea flows up to the town. I deliverd a letter to Dr. Wavell from Dr. Babington and in consequence we dined with him. In the afternoon Dr. W shewed us some fine views in the Neighbourhood. Golden Lion an excellent Inn at Barnstaple.

| Bill at Torrington ec. | £0 18 9 |
| Bill at Barnstaple ec. | 1 5 6 |

| half £1 2 0 | £2 4 3 |

SATURDAY MAY 21ST Breakfasted with Dr. Wavell and set out at 9 oClock for South Molton. Dr. W accompanied us as far as a place called High Down above Lary, about one Mile from Lord Fortescue's Seat at Castle Hill, a little to the left of the road leading from Barnstaple to South Molton—at this place is a small hill which is to the South East of Barnstaple. The side of this hill has been broken down for materials to mend the road and exhibits confused strata of black schistus clay mixed with some quartz. Between the flakes of the schistus clay and in the transverse fissures a white radiated substance is found in the form when unbroken of complete hemispheres. This is at present supposed to be a variety of Zeolite.[1] The situation of the strata and other like circumstances could not be observed as the chief part was coverd with the loose fragments. I observed however that even immediately under the grass this crystallized substance was found and that it sometimes formed imperfect intermediate strata with the black schistose clay to the thickness of $\frac{1}{4}$ or $\frac{1}{2}$ of an inch. Within a few yards of this hill is a Pit which affords a whitish or white softer schistose clay with Zones and Veins of a reddish yellow. Near Barnstaple Argills Grey Schistus or Thon Schiefer abounds which passes into Schistose clay or Schiefer Thon at abt 3 Miles or thereabouts from Barnstaple. We took leave of Dr. Wavell at High Down and proceeded to South Molton 12 Miles from B. S Molton is a pretty considerable town, the road to it was hilly but the country beautiful and well cultivated —fine hill and dale. Set out for Tiverton—fine country all the way. Hilly road. Tiverton a large town in a beautiful situation; arrived there by 4 oClock 19 Miles from S Molton. Dined there and set out for Taunton. Near Tiverton I observed the same red soil as at Exeter and its neighbourhood. Near Tiverton the thick slaty banks on the road side are of the same colour. Every circumstance confirms me in my first idea that much of this red soil is produced by the decomposition of a greyish chlorit schiefer or killas. This decomposition takes place in the superior strata—Mr. Savaresi is now of my opinion.

The road from Tiverton to Taunton is excellent and thro a most beautiful and fertile country diversified with Hills and Dales. Entered Somersetshire at Wellington 7 Miles from Taunton and arrived at Taunton 21 Miles by 8 oClock. Taunton a large and upon the whole a well built town. Supd and slept at the Castle Inn.

[1] The mineral which Dr. Wavell showed to Hatchett was later analysed by Sir Humphrey Davy and at the suggestion of Dr. Babington, it was called Wavellite; it is a hydrated phosphate of aluminium.

		£	s	d
Chaise to S Molton 12 M		£0	14	0
Driver		0	2	0
Chaise to Tiverton 19 M		1	2	2
Driver		0	3	0
Dinner & waiter		0	4	0
Hostlers at B SM & T		0	1	6
Turnpikes		0	3	6
Chaise to Taunton 21 M		1	4	6
Driver		0	3	0
half £1 18 10		£3	17	8

SUNDAY MAY 22ND Set out at 10 oClock for Bridgewater, fine road and country. Schistus and red soil still to be observed—reached Bridgewater 12 M by 12 oClock—Bridgewater is famous for good Bricks. It has a quay. Set out again for Axbridge at 2 oClock; on leaving Bridgewater the character of the calcareous Earth began to appear on the road, and a slaty limestone of a pale brownish grey colour was digged up out of some Pits by the roadside. From Bridgewater to Axbridge the road is in an extensive flat Plain bounded by the Mendip Hills. Dined at New Cross 18 M near Axbridge. After dinner set out for Wells and viewed the Chedder cliffs, an immense chasm divides the Mendip Hills for near 1 & $\frac{1}{2}$ or 2 miles in a transverse section. On each side the rocks of black & blackish brown Limestone veined with white Calc: Spar appear to a great height. One rock is 340 feet perpendicular. There are several Caverns with Stalactites. The strata are from one foot to 2 or 3; their direction is from North West to South East and their dip or inclination is from North East to South West. Several springs rise at the base of these rocks and form in a short distance a small river. Arrived at Wells 12 M by 8 oClock—fine country all about. The road was on the side of the Mendip Hills.

		£	s	d
Bill at Taunton		£0	16	6
Chaise to Bridgewater 12m		0	14	0
Driver		0	2	0
Hostler		0	0	6
Turnpikes		0	2	0
Chaise to Axbridge 18 M		1	1	0
Driver		0	2	6

Hostler	0	0	6
Turnpikes	0	1	0
Driver	0	2	2
Dinner	0	7	0
Chaise to Wells 14 M	0	16	4
Gave at Chedder	0	1	0
half £2 3 3	£4	6	6

MONDAY MAY 23RD   At 10 oClock AM set out from Wells for Bath 20 miles—the country fine with much hill and dale. Road mended with Pale grey limestone till about 8 miles of Bath. The Limestone is coverd and intermixed with red earth like that which coated the Mendip Hills near Chedder, perhaps Manganese or Calamine may contribute to this colour. At about the 8 Mile Stone the limestone became whiter and at about 4 & $\frac{1}{2}$ miles from Bath nearly quite white with an upper stratum of chalk under the grass. As schistus is the prevailing substance in Devonshire so is Limestone in this part of Somersetshire and in many places near the limits of the two counties schistose Marle appeared and formed an evident passage from the Argillaceous into the Calcareous genus. The Bath Stone may be cut with a saw but becomes harder by time. At Bath they use for flagstones a grey Micaceous Argillaceous Grit from Hannam near Bristol.

Bill etc at Wells	£	14	0
Post to Bath 20 M	1	3	4
Turnpikes	0	2	0
Driver	0	3	0
	£2	2	4

TUESDAY MAY 24TH   Bath is nearly surrounded with mountains of Limestone. The Bath Stone is a species of Oolites occasionally mixed with some Calc: Spar and fragments etc of some small shells which occasion some difference in the degree of hardness in different masses, or even in parts of the same mass. The neighbourhood also affords a grey limestone which often contains shells and sometimes Pyrites which I have seen crystallized in 8dral crystals.

Round Bath at the distance of 6 and 10 Miles are various coal

Mines which afford coal of a good quality which is burned at Bath. The Mendip Hills in the vicinity yield Lead, Calamine and Manganese.

WEDNESDAY MAY 25TH Set out from Bath at 11 oClock AM for Bristol. Within a Mile of Bath at a Place called Weston are some Mills for extending and making concave Brass Plates for Vessels— these mills belong to Messrs Harford & Co at Bristol. Near the Mills in about ½ or ¾ of a Mile passed a coal Pit. Stopped at Keynsham 5 miles from Bristol to see the Mills for making Brass Wire and Plates also belonging to Messrs Harford but were not permitted to see them as we had not a letter from the committee. Arrived at Bristol by 1 oClock, went to the Bush Inn. After dinner went to the Hot Wells and St. Vincents Rocks. These rocks are chiefly composed of a bluish or brownish grey hard Lime Stone veined with white Calc: Spar. The strata vary in thickness from 12 or 18 inches to much more. The direction of the strata appears to be nearly North East to South West and the dip or inclination is from North West to South East. The fissures and divisions of the upper Strata are coated with a red ochry matter & in cavities quartz is found crystallized on Hematites and sometimes on the limestone. Small particles of Galena are found disseminated in the sparry veins. The upper strata are generally of a bluish tinge and make better Lime than the lower strata which are brownish and smell much of Bitumen when rubbed. In these latter Veins of a whitish grey flint are found. This stone is used partly for lime and also sometimes to build. A great part is likewise consumed in mending the roads and for ballast. Went to Kings Weston and called on Mr. Lewis at Shire Hampton.

	£		
Bill etc at Bath	£3	0	6
Post to Bristol 14 M	0	16	4
Driver	0	2	2
Turnpikes	0	1	9
Driver to Kings Weston	0	2	0
Gave when at the rocks	0	1	0
	£4	3	9

N.B. the Mills at Weston near Bath have small Hammers worked by a water wheel and the plates are heated each time in a sort of Oven or Furnace.

THURSDAY MAY 26TH   At Bristol there is a Manufactory for making Brass, also for Sulphuric Acid and for Sal Ammoniac, the latter belong to a Mr. Jn Cave a Druggist in Redcliff Street and the former to Messrs Harford & Co. Met with a degree of illiberality which characterises Bristol—we were refused admittance by the proprietors at the Brass Manufactory. It is said that they roast zinc ore called Blende or Black Jack and use it instead of Calamine.

Bill at Bristol   £2 18   0

Bush Inn—the South or South West Gate of B towards the Hot Wells is Saxon—in good preservation.

FRIDAY MAY 27TH   Set out from Bristol at $\frac{1}{2}$ past 10 oClock good road and the country well cultivated Limestone mixed with red earth appeared in several places—arrived at Newport 18 M—a village—by one oClock. Near Newport the limestone changes to a sort of grey reddish Argillaceous Schistose Grit mixed with calc: earth and small particles of spar. A dark green substance is also occasionally mixed with it. Set out for Gloucester 16 M and arrived there by $\frac{1}{2}$ past 3 oClock—good road and cultivated country—near Gloucester the soil at 2 or 3 feet under the gravel is a pale soft bluish Marle as appeared in the Canal called the Berkeley Canal which is now making and carrying on towards Gloucester and at present is within about $\frac{1}{4}$ of a Mile from the City. Dined at the Bell Inn at Gloucester.

The Cathedral is partly Saxon in the interior. The Saxon arches are supported by columns of an immense bulk. Set out for Tewksbury at $\frac{1}{2}$ past 5 oClock—fine country and good road. The roads here are repaired with an indurated pale blue Marle. Arrived at Tewksbury 11 M by $\frac{1}{2}$ past 8 oClock. No beds to be had on account of the contested Election similar to that at Bristol; went on to Worcester 15 M and arrived there by $\frac{1}{2}$ past 10 oClock. Slept at the Star and Garter. Fine Gothic tower of the Cathedral at Gloucester. Fine Saxon window in Tewksbury church.

SATURDAY MAY 28TH   Worcester is a considerable city but not so large as Bristol—went to see the Porcelain Manufactory belonging to Messrs Flight & Barr. I have observed that the Steatites of Cornwall is used as an ingredient but could not learn the other component parts of the paste or clay (perhaps it is the decomposed

Feldtspar from St. Stephen in Cornwall). When the steatite is reduced to powder in a mill at Worcester it is sent to some place about 10 miles distant to be mixed and washed; it is then brought back to W and in a liquid state is passed thro fine wire seives, is dried, and then temperd with water for use. When the ware is moulded it is of a brownish white or very pale brown; it is then gently and imperfectly dryed. The bottoms and edges are then turned in a laithe and the Ribs if required are formed by pressing it in a Mould. The edges are then Scalloped with a knife. The ware is then perfectly dryed and is baked in a kiln, inclosed in pans of coarse clay. It then comes out in the state called Biscuit. If it is to be painted blue (with cobalt) this is then done and the ware is again baked and then dipped into the glazing liquid which is of a pale red (perhaps contains Minium). The ware is then baked again and the blue colour strikes thro the glazing. If gold or any other colour than blue is to be used these are applied after the ware is glazed. The colours appear to be ground with oil of Turpentine. The gold appears to be used in the state of Cassius's Precipitate. When the ware is painted with this it is put into a small square brick Furnace and is arranged in a square Iron Pan which has an Iron Cover with a Pipe. On this cover kindled charcoal is put till the Top is full. The gold when the ware comes out of this Furnace is of a dead buff colour and is burnished by women with Burnishers made of Agate or Hematites. The fuel used in the kilns is a light Pit Coal in large Masses with the appearance of charred wood in many places—this is brought from some Miles distance in the county of Worcester. Sometimes instead of pencilling the ware they used engraved copper Plates which they fill up with the colouring matter, then with rollers take off the impression on a sort of soft tissue paper which they then apply to the ware and rub with cushions of flannel.

After dinner set out for Bromsgrove—road good and well cultivated country. The soil at about 4 or 5 Miles from W of a deep red with some thin veins of blue Marle. Near Bromsgrove I observed large strata of a reddish soft Argillaceous Grit. Bromsgrove is a small town 13 Miles from Worcester. Set out for Birmingham, crossed a Heath—observed very fine loose brownish white Argillaceous Grit. The calcareous character must therefore have ceased somewhere between Tewksbury and Worcester which I could not observe on account of the night. Arrived at Birmingham by 8 oClock. Called on Mr. Holden and slept at the Hen & Chickens.

	£	s	d
Post to Newport 18 M	£1	1	0
Driver	0	2	6
Turnpikes	0	1	0
Post to Gloucester 16 M	0	18	8
Driver	0	2	4
Turnpikes	0	1	3
Bill at Gloucester etc	0	6	3
Post to Tewksbury 11 M	0	12	10
Driver	0	2	0
Post to Worcester 15 M at 1s.	0	15	0
Driver	0	2	2
Turnpikes	0	2	6
	4	17	6
Bill at Worcester	1	1	3
Post to Bromsgrove 13 M	0	13	0
Driver	0	2	0
Turnpikes	0	1	0
Post to Birmingham 13 M	0	13	0
Driver	0	2	0
Turnpikes	0	1	6
Gave at Porcelain Manufactory	0	2	6
	7	13	9
Bill at Bristol	2	18	0
half £5 5 10½	£10	11	9

SUNDAY MAY 29TH Breakfasted with Mr. Holden in New Street. Dined at our Inn (the Hen & Chickens) and in short loitered away the day.

MONDAY MAY 30TH Went with Mr. Holden after Breakfast to Mr. Boulton's at Soho 2 miles from Birmingham to see the Manufactory. At present about 400 Persons Men Women and Children are employed but before the Steam Engines occupied so much of Mr. B's attention there were 700 in the Manufactory. Here we saw the various operations on Buttons, Buckles, Plated and Steel Wares etc partly worked by Machines and partly by hand. The whole cannot easily be described but is a wonderful establishment especially as it has been made by one Man.

Called to see the Painted Glass near Mr. Boulton's at Mr. Eggington's who painted the windows in Salisbury Cathedral. Dine with Mr. Holden in company with Mr. Nott the Priest of the Roman Catholic chapel. After dinner went with Mr. Simcox one of the principal proprietors of the Brass Furnaces to see the works. In these works they use granulated copper mixed with Calamine from Somersetshire, Wales, Derbyshire and Yorkshire which has been on the spot calcined Picked and Pulverised.

The works, beside the rooms for meeting of the Proprietors and the Magazine, consists of four Buildings each of which contain 6 Furnaces three of which are separated from the other three by a Wall. These Furnaces are circular about 4 feet in Diameter and about the same in height. Above the ash hole is a cast iron bottom with Holes and the bodies of these Furnaces are below the level of the pavement of the houses.

In each Furnace nine large Crucibles are Placed, one much larger than the rest being in the centre. The Calamine and copper being mixed and covered with charcoal or perhaps in this case with Pit coal or saw dust, the whole is well roasted and at length melted in the course of 12 hours (for they make two operations in 24 hours) when the Brass is ready to be poured into moulds. They arrange a number of Cast Iron Moulds and remove the largest crucible out of the Furnace, from this they take out the superincumbent ashes etc  leaving enough to keep the Zinc from burning and then stir the melted matter with an Iron Rod. Afterwards they take out the other crucibles, take off the ashes and stir each as it comes out and then pour the contents one after the other into the large crucible which just is able to hold the whole quantity of the melted Brass contained in the nine crucibles. They then by means of two Men with an instrument take up this crucible and fill the moulds. The 9 crucibles of each Furnace contain

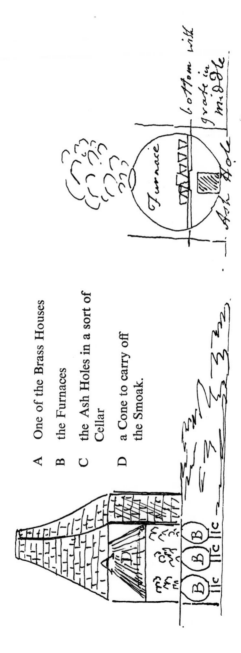

A   One of the Brass Houses

B   the Furnaces

C   the Ash Holes in a sort of
    Cellar

D   a Cone to carry off
    the Smoak.

Brass furnaces at Birmingham

about 6 lb of Brass and as there are 6 Furnaces in each of the four Melting Houses they all (that is 24 Furnaces) make every 12 hours

about   76   456
              6   4
           ___
           456   1824 of Brass. The Men do not suffer in Health.

Mr. Savaresi thinks that the Germans do better in using larger crucibles and in having copper plates instead of granulated copper. These Plates the Germans stratify with the Calamine. The fuel used in these Melting Houses is a Pit Coal of a good quality which is brought from about 8 or 9 miles from Birmingham.

Birmingham is a very large and upon the whole a well built town —in size it is however inferior to Bristol.

TUESDAY MAY 31ST   In the morning at $\frac{1}{2}$ past 8 went with Mr. Holden to see a curious Machine at Mr. May's a whip maker. The machine is worked by children and one person with one of these machines can do more and work better than could formerly be done by 4 Persons. This machine is said to plat the twist over Horse whips etc and was invented some years ago by a common whip maker. Breakfasted with Mr. Holden and afterwards went to see Mr. Clay's Manufactory for the Paper Buttons etc. This ware is not made by reducing the Paper to a Pulp but is formed by pasting sheets of whitish brown paper on each other till the proper thickness is produced; the Trays etc are then made out of the Boards thus made and the rest of the work is like that of the cabinet makers.

We then went to Mr. Geo. Simcox's in Livery Street where we saw one of the most singular species of Manufacture viz of white metal Buckles, Curtain Rings and especially of finger Rings with Mock coloured stones or Plain of Brass or Tin. The work is expeditiously performed by many women, children and some men—the Rings with coloured stones do not sell for more than about two thirds of a farthing each and the plain ones about one Penny per grose (or 12 Doz). The Buckles of white metal when chased of a handsome pattern sell at 6d per Pair with tongues and chapes. One of the women employed in casting these buckles in hand Moulds (as Boys cast Dumps) told me that she had 5d for 12 Doz pairs. The finger Rings and Buckles are sent to Spain and nearly over the world according to Mr. Simcox's account.

Set out at 12 oClock from Birmingham passed thro Wednesbury 8 Miles from B—a long town with many Iron Forges and Coal works. The coal is of a good quality and I observed on leaving Birmingham a pale reddish grit or sandstone like that mentioned at Bromsgrove—the upper stratum here as well as near Birmingham and Wednesbury was gravel. Arrived at Wolverhampton 14 miles from Birmingham—a large town where great quantities of Iron Utensils for Kitchens etc are made. Dined at W set out at ½ past 3 for Shiffnall passed thro a beautiful country—observed that the same grit appeared in many places; arrived at Shiffnall 12 Miles by ½ past 5 oClock. Set out for Coal Brook Dale—the country all the way very fine. The grit often was seen and especially in the neighbourhood of the coal works so that this grit may probably be regarded as a symptom of the presence of coal. The descent to Coal Brook Dale is wonderfully beautiful and romantic.

	£1	12	9
Bill at Birmingham	£1	12	9
Post to Wolverhampton 14 M	0	14	0
Driver	0	2	0
Bill at Wolverhampton	0	7	3
Post to Shiffnall 12 M	0	12	0
Driver	0	2	0
Post to Coal Brook Dale 7 M	0	7	0
Driver	0	1	6
Turnpikes	0	2	6
half £2 0 6	£4	1	0

WEDNESDAY JUNE 1ST   Coal Brook Dale or at least the principal Iron Foundery is situated on the Northern side of the Severn about one Mile from the Banks but on each side of the river are a great number of houses in different large groups which all called by different names—these are inhabited chiefly by People more or less concerned in the different Iron and Coal works which are here very numerous. The Banks of the Severn on either side are flanked by Mountains beautifully wooded and the appearance is uncommonly Picturesque and Romantic. The River near the Iron Bridge runs from about NW to SE it is not very broad but rapid.

This place has the remarkable advantage of finding in the mountains on the banks of the river Iron Ore, Coal and (in the neighbourhood) Lime Stone so that Nature has here supplied every requisite material for Smelting the ores of Iron. In the morning after Breakfast we went to see the Principal Iron Foundery called the Dale Works the situation of which I have mentioned—these belong to a Quaker Family of the name of Darby which by marriage is connected with another Quaker family of the name of Reynolds which is in possession of most of the other great works, and I was informed by the old Quaker who shewed us the works that in the district belonging to these two families between 30 and 40,000 souls are supported either by working in the Founderies or in the Iron & Coal Mines. The Furnaces of these works are about 30 feet high and the Blast is produced by large cylinders instead of bellows. The Furnace is charged at the top with the Ore (which has been roasted) mingled with Lime Stone for the flux—the fuel is Coak which they make upon the spot by partially charring or burning the Pit coal covered with Earth and Ashes. They tap the Furnace twice in the course of a Day and each time cast between 3 and 4 Tons (20,000 to the Ton) of Iron. The metal is by a channel made in Sand conveyed into a sort of trough of Iron which serves as a reservoir out of which they Ladle it into different Moulds. When all these are filled they raise the back of the Trough by a Crane and Hook so that the remainder of the Iron is poured into another channel formed in sand which has a number of shorter running laterally from it thus the long one is called the Sow and the short ones the Pigs. Some of the Pig Iron is worked under the great hammers in the Forges belonging to  this establishment into Bar Iron or into Stamps for Stamping Mills and the rest is melted again for casting vessels and other utensils in an Air Furnace in which the flame is reverberated.

A is that by which the metal to be melted is introduced.

B is that by which the melted metal is laded

C is the door by which the Fuel is put in

In this Furnace also they melt the scrap Iron or
the small fragments in pots of this shape.

There are two of the great High Furnaces—these are
internally in the form of a double cone. The fuel in the
Forges is the Pit coal. The Celebrated Iron Bridge over
the Severn was cast in this Foundry and they have made
one to be fixed at Bridgewater. They have also begun a
third for themselves. After dinner we went to see Mr. Brodies
Foundery for cannon (all of 32 Pounders). The Cannon are moulded
in 4 pieces which are afterwards joined. The cannon when cast are
solid and the weight of two (which is the number cast at each time)
is 7 Tons 12 Cwt. The cannon are then (by a square piece formed at
the Breach) fixed in a mortice in the centre of a cogged wheel which
is turned by a Steam Engine (7 or 8 are worked
at one time) the extra pieces at the Muzzles are
then cut off by a hard sharp Plate of steel and
they are then bored. The borer by an ingenious
and simple contrivance is made by weights and a carriage to advance
on a rack work in proportion as it penetrates the Cannon.

N.B. there are 5 pieces including the Head which is cut off.
This foundery of Mr. Brodies is about one mile and a ½ SE of the
Iron Bridge on the SW bank of the River.
Near Mr. Brodies Foundery is a Building erected by Lord Dundonald [1] for the Distilling of Pit coal—by this process the Bitumenous
part of the coal (which is lost in the usual way of making Coak) is
conveyed through long winding chimneys and after being condensed
is received in a Recipient.

---

[1] Lord Dundonald was also a partner with Losh in chemical works on Tyneside
and had collieries in east Scotland. At Calcote he set up coke ovens between
1780 and 1790; was interested in making coal gas and its byproducts. In 1793
he was the first Scottish coal owner to stop the employment underground of
boys and women.

A is the Door of a Round Kiln or
    Furnace

B is the circular Aperture closed by an
    Iron cover.

CC are iron registers to regulate the
    combustion of the coal.

D is the bottom of the kiln with a small
    circular grate in the middle.

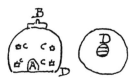

Under the bottom D of the Kiln is a sort of a cellar by which (when some wood and chips are placed over the grate at D and the kiln filled up with 5 Tons of coal[1]) fire is communicated to the Pile. The Door A and the Top B are closely shut and the combustion being regulated by the registers CCCC the smoke cannot escape but by a chimney inclined rather laterally near the top which chimney at first is in this form and then opens into a flue which returns several times 7, 8 or 9 times and is covered with lead over which is a shallow depth of 9 inches or so of water. This winding flue at length at E which is inclined communicates with a perpendicular pipe which conveys the condensed Petroleum into a Receptacle below. The more to condense the smoke Tiles are placed in this flue thus dividing the internal capacity. The extreme end of the flue terminates in an upright chimney to carry off the small portion of uncondensed smoke.

The Tar or Petroleum is boiled and occasionally brought to the consistency of Pitch. During the boiling the Oil which rises is also condensed and received by a smaller but similar apparatus. This oil is also sometimes rectified in an Alembic and Worm Tub.

On the NE Bank of the river nearly opposite to Mr. Brodies but rather farther from the Iron Bridge is a Tunnel cut in the side of a Mountain of whitish Argillaceous Grit which is about 1040 yds long and into which we penetrated abt 760 yds—in this gallery or tunnel Petroleum is found which drips through the grit into a small rill of water from the top of which it is collected. The lower part of the Sand stone or Grit is penetrated with the Petroleum which now sells

[1] 5 tons produce 2 Barrels of Tar/36 Gallons each. (ft.note as in MS.)

for 5 guineas the Barrel (36 gallons) part of this is rectified on the spot to make British Oil. This Gallery communicates with a Coal Mine of considerable depth. About 100 yds from this last place is a Porcelain Manufactory lately established. The ware is like that of Worcester and the materials the same.

The Mountains which form the banks of the Severn at Coalbrook Dale are lofty and are sloped rapidly towards the river. A little above the Dale to the NW the mountains open on each side towards a Plain. It is in these Mountains that the iron ore and coal are found in a wonderful abundance. The coal is often found over the Iron Ore but the latter never over the former. The Iron and Coal Mines are often by the side of each other within the distance sometimes of a few yards. The superior strata over the Iron as well as the coal Mines is a fine white or whitish Argillaceous Grit or sandstone which sometimes becomes schistose and is often veined with the Iron Ore or the coal especially when it is in contact so as to form the walls of the veins.

The Ore is a pale brown Argillaceous Iron Ore (Thonartiger Eisenstein) occasionally mixed with Calc: Spar or with coal. This Iron Ore also contains the remains of Vegetables as well as impressions of them and every part about Coalbrook Dale bears evident marks of a deposit formed by water (many large masses of Breccias and Puddingstones). The Iron Ore is not rich in quality but this is compensated by the quantity and the ease with which it is obtained. Many of the coal and iron Mines are entered by lateral Galleries as they here call them—Tunnels. The Tontine or Iron Bridge Inn very excellent.

Iron rail roads invented by Mr. John Curr of Sheffield are made here for the coal works also the Inclined Planes. The ropes which move the Corves or Carts on these are worked by a small Steam Engine, first used here now also at Attercliffe Colliery near Sheffield.

THURSDAY JUNE 2ND After Breakfast set out and returned to Shiffnall 7 M and from thence proceeded to Newport 8 M. The reddish loose Grit appeared in several places both on going and leaving Newport (which is a small town) the country about it is plain and open. Dined at Eccleshall 9 M also a small town and proceeded to Newcastle under Lyne 13 M—white and reddish grit still prevailed. Went to the Buck Inn. Bad accommodation.

FRIDAY JUNE 3RD   Breakfasted with Mrs. Byerby and then went to see Mr. Wedgwoods Pottery at Etruria about 1½ miles to the E of Newcastle. The Queens Ware is made of a mixture of clay from Devonshire and Dorsetshire and a certain proportion of Calcined Flints. This mixture is much diluted with water then passed thro fine lawn sieves and nearly dried by evaporation. The glazing is done with white Oxyd of Lead.

At one oClock PM set out and arrived at Uttoxeter by ½ past 4 oClock. N.B. Newcastle and a Large Borough Town where they make great quantities of Hats on the road to Uttoxeter. The Grit appeared in several places. Dined at Uttoxeter 19 M set out through a flat plain open country in general and good road. Reached Derby 19 M by ½ past 8 oClock.

	£		
Bill at Coalbrookdale	£1	17	6
Gave at the Founderies	0	13	6
Post to Shiffnall 7 M 1s2	0	8	2
Driver	0	1	10
Newport 9 M	0	8	0
Driver	0	2	0
Eccleshall 9 M	0	9	0
Driver	0	1	6
Dinner	0	6	0
Newcastle 13 M	0	13	0
Driver	0	2	0
Ch. maid	0	2	0
Boots	0	0	6
Uttoxeter 19 M 1s1d	1	0	7
Driver	0	2	6
Dinner	0	6	0
Derby 19 M	1	0	7
Driver	0	2	6
Turnpikes	0	3	0
Gave at pottery	0	3	0
half £4 1 7	£8	3	2

SATURDAY JUNE 4TH   Derby is a pretty large Town but not handsome, it is pleasantly situate in a plain which rather is depressed in the middle. There is a Manufactory of good Porcelain carried on by Mr. Duesbury. After breakfast we set out from the Bell (a very comfortable Inn) the country on leaving Derby was rather flat but fine as we advanced towards Wirksworth the country was very beautiful and finely diversified with Hill and Dale. The soil is gravel under which the Grit so often mentioned appears, but the grains of quartz more distinct and larger than in the former cases, and also the degree of coherence much greater. Near Wirksworth the Limestone began to appear, and continued all the day afterwards. Passed thro Wirksworth 14 Mls from D. moderately large Town also passed several Cotton Mills belonging to Mr. Arkwright whose elegant seat and one of the most considerable Mills is within 1 & ½ miles of Matlock. The approach to Matlock is romantic and the descent to it very steep. Matlock is a small place consisting of a few houses situated in a most romantic spot on the banks of the River Derwent the mountains on each side are high and of a hard pale brown bituminous limestone approaching to Marble. The beds or strata have their direction from N to S their dip or inclination from West to East nearly. Near Matlock are several Mines particularly of lead the white spathose Lead and Calamine in the form of Calc Spar is found in these Mines. Near Matlock I found some Toadstone. Went to the old Baths kept by Mason—curious machine for sawing and polishing Marble at Mr. Browns.

Bill etc at Derby	£0	9	0
Post to Matlock 17 mls at 1s. 1d.	0	18	5
Driver	0	2	7
Turnpikes	0	1	0
half £0 15 6	£1	11	0

SUNDAY JUNE 5TH The Limestone about Matlock is grey or brownish grey and is much impregnated with Bitumen—between the strata of the Limestone, strata of chert are seen. The Matlock Waters have no perceptible taste and are about the temperature of 68 of Fahrenheit, they flow thro the Toad Stone. The River Derwent famous for Trout and Grayling. After dinner set out for Ashover 6 miles, road very hilly. Slept at Mr. Milnes the Agent for the Mines belonging to Sir Jos Banks.

Bill at Matlock	£1	5	0
Post to Ashover 6 miles	1	6	6
Driver	0	1	0
Turnpikes	0	1	0
half £0 16 9	£1	13	6

MONDAY JUNE 6TH   Ashover is a small village situate in a valley surrounded by Hills. These hills are in respect to their upper strata siliceous grit under which is shale or black schistus which is followed

by Limestone. The bottom of the valley is Toadstone. At about $\frac{1}{2}$ or $\frac{3}{4}$ of a mile to the West of the village of Ashover is a Lead Mine called West Edge which is not at present very promising, the ore is galena mixed with steel grained ore (Antimoniated Lead) in Fluor and Calc: Spar. The Ore is dispersed in it very much in small particles or portions at best for the greater part. The country is limestone interrupted by strata of Toadstone. Slickensides is found here, both black and white, the black explodes. Blende is also found (a bad sign) it is also deemed bad when the Slickensides disappears. The mine is now 35 fathoms deep—has a common Steam Engine. At about 1 & $\frac{1}{2}$ miles to South of Ashover is a Lead Mine called Cock Well. The ore here is the common galena; 75 fathoms deep. At about 2 miles or 1 & $\frac{3}{4}$ to south is Gregory Hillock Mine the most celebrated Lead mine in Derbyshire—produced £140,000 at the first working without any expence to the Proprietors. This mine is now 150 fathoms deep—it has a common Steam Engine and also one of Boulton's (Mr. Milnes prefers the former) for heavy work—also a third common Steam Engine to draw the Ore. The Ore is galena mixed with the Antimoniated Ore like that of West Edge.

The Toadstone appears to have a base of Wakké—it becomes very soft by being exposed to the Air & Weather. The Veins in all these mines run E & W and dip or Hade to North. The limestone which is the matrix is in all these mines the Lapis Smilus or Stink Stein (Query if general in Derbyshire?). Garnets are found in some of these grits The Limestone with Entrochi often passes into chert. The Toadstones vary much in appearance, colour and texture. In Derbyshire they call Pipe Veins those which go down deep

and those rake veins which spread thus Fluor, Calc: spar, Cawk and Quartz are found in these mines, occasionally mixed with the Toadstone.

Post to Ashover half from Matlock	3			
Chatsworth	13			
Bakewell	7	1	6	7
	—			
Miles	23			
Dinner		0	2	11
Turnpikes		0	2	6
Gave at Chatsworth		0	8	6
Half £1 0 3		£2	0	6

From Ashover we went to Chatsworth the road bad and sandy. The house at Chatsworth did not answer my expectations—proceeded to Bakewell where we slept.

TUESDAY JUNE 7TH   In the morning saw part of Mr. White Watson's[1] collection of Fossils—this is a Geographical Mineral collection relative to Derbyshire and does Mr. W. W. much credit. It appears that Grit forms the upper stratum of the Derbyshire Mountains in general under which are found coal and Iron stone (Thonartiger Eisenstein). These are succeeded by fine black shale or schistus then limestone after which Toadstone occurs alternatively with Limestone.

[1] White Watson called himself a sculptor and made funeral monuments. He was a good geologist and established a shop in Bakewell from which he sold marble and spar ornaments and collections (usually of 500) of Derbyshire mineral specimens. He is well known for the geological sections of the Derbyshire mineral field and of Greenhow Hill, Yorkshire, made by inlaying into limestone, thin sections of the true rocks and minerals depicted. Sixteen examples of these are known, ten in museums, three at Chatsworth, two in my own collection and one other. Reference should be made to "White Watson (1760-1835) and his Geological Sections." T. D. Ford. *Proc. Geol. Assoc.* 71 (1960). 349-63.

In the Grit and the upper strata abundance of Vegetable and Animal Petrifactions and Impressions are met with. Towards the (*sic* in MS) of Bakewell about ¼ of a Mile from the Town the limestone forms the upper strata without any grit; this limestone is grey & brownish grey and is very bituminous. The strata here of the limestone fall East and West and appear as if Moulded on a hillock of Toadstone thus:

This Toadstone is in some places nearly solid in others either filled with nodules of Calc: spar or is become cellular by the decomposition of these nodules. The part which is exposed to the Air is soft, and brown more or less of an Ochry colour—there can be no doubt but that the Toadstone is a species of the Amygdaloides or Mandelstein and the base of it is Argillaceous and evidently that substance called Wacke. The stone found at Thorverton near Exeter is of the same nature. The stone also which we found at Newport between Bristol and Gloucester appears to be a variety of this species.

Steatites is also found in Derbyshire and is employed in the Porcelain Manufactory at Derby. Granite has been found but as it was only seldom and in small detached blocks there is no positive reason to conclude that it forms mountains in this county. The grit about Ashover is white but it sometimes became yellow and Ochry as I observed on the road to Chatsworth. Dined with Mr. Thos. Barker and saw his collection—Mr. B. is proprietor of some Lead Smelting Works 6 miles from Bakewell.

WEDNESDAY JUNE 8TH Set out from Bakewell at 11 o'clock went across the Country to see the Ecton Mine which is in Staffordshire— by the road we went it was 13 miles from Bakewell to Ecton.

Ecton is in Staffordshire on the borders of Derbyshire—it is a small village but is remarkable for a rich copper and lead mine which goes by the name of the Ecton Mine and is the sole property of the Duke of Devonshire. Till the year 1760 it was leased to a company but has since been worked only for the profit and at the expence of the Duke. It is said when very rich to have afforded to him about £30,000 per Annm at present it is on the decline--the total depth is 200 fathoms from the top of the mountain on which the Steam Engine (one of Boulton's) is placed. At the bottom of this Mountain which is 25 fathoms in height is a level by which the Mine may be commodiously enter'd and by which much of the Ore is drawn out in small carts with horses. In this level is a machine or Balance Bob which is worked by a Tub which is filled with water at top and empties itself by a Valve when it descends—this raises the Ore in a barrel. There is a similar machine which works some Pump Rods—the country of this mine is a brownish sparry granular not Bituminous limestone, interrupted by strata of Toadstone. The Copper Ore is chiefly yellow but part is also the pulverulent green ore and part the Hepatic Ore which they reckon the best. The Copper Ore is mixed with galena and Brown Blende—the latter did not appear to be known in the Mine till I pointed it out altho' in considerable quantities. The galena is in a great quantity. At this Mine they roast the copper ore but do not smelt it. The galena is not now smelted here but it is carried to near Cheadle, but the lead slag is here worked over again in what is called a Slag Hearth worked with bellows. The second slag contains copper and is again smelted for it. From Ecton we proceeded to Buxton which is 15 Miles from Ecton—Buxton is a small ill built Town or Village situated in a valley but is much decorated by the Crescent & Stables built by the Duke of Devonshire.

THURSDAY JUNE 9TH   Buxton is chiefly remarkable for its Baths and Waters the temperature is 82 of Farenheit. The Waters has little or no taste. At about $\frac{3}{4}$ of a Mile from B is Pooles Hole an extensive cavern about 665 yds long and contains white Calc. Sparry Stalactites in many shapes which receive as many fanciful names such as the Flitch of Bacon, the Queen of Scots, Pillar etc.—set out at 12 o'clock very hilly road.   Near Castleton the country very romantic. Castleton is 12 Miles from Buxton and is a small Town at the foot of the Peak—went to the Castle Inn. After dinner went to see the famous cavern called the Devil's Arse the extent is—for a further description see Pilkington's Hist: of Derbyshire[1] & letters concerning a Tour thro England etc by Sullivan.

Bill etc at Bakewell	£1	3	0
Post to Ecton & Buxton 28 mls	1	10	4
Driver	0	3	2

[1] Pilkington, J. *A View of the present state of Derbyshire.* 2 vols. 1789.

Turnpikes	0	1	6
Gave at Ecton	0	3	0
Bill at Buxton	0	15	0
Gave at Pooles Hole etc	0	5	0
At Baths & Pump Room	0	2	0
Post to Castleton 12 m.	0	14	0
Driver	0	2	0
Turnpikes	0	0	6
Expences for seeing the Peak	0	15	0

half £2 17 3   £5 14 6

The stalactites in the Peak are white spar as in Pooles Hole—the general mass is brownish sparry limestone (not bituminous).

FRIDAY JUNE 10TH Went in the morning to see a remarkable Lead Mine called the Speedwell Mine which is about $\frac{1}{2}$ of a Mile to the West of Castleton on the Manchester road.

There is a shaft 12 fathoms deep by which the Ore is drawn up but the descent into the Mine is by an opening in the side of a hill from which a flight of 106 stone steps go down to the aforesaid depth of 12 fathoms. We then came to a Canal of water on which was a flat bottomed Boat—we were then worked thro the Canal by pieces of wood fixed in the sides of the rock by which the Boatmen held so as to pull the Boat forwards. In this manner we went for about 700 yards and then came into a Cavern so lofty that we could not discern the roof altho the Boatmen clambered up a considerable height on the rock with candles. In this place the surface or grass is rather more than 300 yards above the level of the canal. The canal runs NE and SWest. When we had thus passed about 650 or 700 yards into the cavern abovementioned we found a cascade which rushes thro a stone dam and falls about 14 yards into a standing water from which the rock goes shelving down to a depth not known. This cascade can be increased by the raising of a plug, the noise being reverberated by the caverns is very great and the effect certainly awful. In this canal are in all as they said 20 of these Cascades larger or smaller but we only saw three—few Persons go beyond the first cascade but we went in all about 1200 yards and were then stopped by a bank of sand. The people said that at times a Boat might go about 300 yards farther and that then there was a way made by planks to go on foot about 300 yards more—from this by climbing up about 300 yards there was an opening to the Day, but if they kept on the level they could go about 1 & ½ miles beyond the planks, by wading thro the water but beyond this was a sort of lake too deep to be forded. The extent therefore of this cavern is not known. The first part of the canal as far as the cavern in which is the first cascade has been made for conveying the Ore of the mine under the shaft, and also about 600 yards beyond the cavern, after which the whole is as formed by Nature. The water is the same which runs thro the Peak probably after it has passed this Mine.

The Mine has not been worked for some time but has lately been purchased by a Mr. Needham who now intends to attempt it again. Hitherto the profits have not been adequate to the expence. This mine is generally known by the name of the Staffordshire Speedwell Mine, because it was begun by a company of Staffordshire gentlemen. The height of the Arch of the artificial passage is about 6 feet above the level of the water—it has been blown with powder. The stone is a brownish sparry granulated limestone veined sometimes with white spar. I did not observe any stalactites.

Castleton is a poor looking place and the chief part of the inhabitants are miners or turners of Derbyshire or Fluor Spar. There are many Lead Mines in the neighbourhood but I question if they are so rich as those at Ashover. One of the lead mines is said to be the oldest in England (but this I doubt) it is called Odin and is to the NW of Castleton. From the top of the mountain it is said to be 150 fathoms deep. In this mine and in another near it the Elastic Bitumen is found and I also procured from a man of the name of Needham (who is the Captn of one of the mines) a new variety of Elastic Bitumen of a pale yellow ochry colour; it has no tenacity and feels and breaks somewhat like soft cawk. It has a bituminous smell but does not burn and crackles and breaks when exposed to the flame of paper. I have some doubt concerning the nature of this substance. [1]

Not far from Odin mine is that which affords the Blue John or Fluor Spar it is called Water Hull (perhaps Hole) the descent into it is by a rough sort of a winding stair case formed by stone steps very

[1] This mineral is probably the one later named *Hatchettite*. Attention was first called to it by the Rev. J. J. Conybeare who described it as occurring in fissures in the clay ironstones of South Wales. This was in 1821 (*Ann. Phil.* 1822.1.136) but Hatchett had noted a similar mineral at other localities many years earlier. It was later analysed by Prof. F. W. Johnstone (*Phil. Mag.* 1838. 12. 338).

rough and slippery by reason of the moisture and abundance of clay. The depth is said to be 65 yards but I think it is much more. The Fluor Spar is found in nodules and strata in a soft yellowish brown clay (strata are in Derbyshire called Pipes and perpendicular Veins are called Rakes) in the caverns are many fine white Calc: Sparry Stalactites—in some places parts of the roof were suspended by these stalactites. This is the Mine which affords all the Fluor Spar which is turned into Vases etc and is said to be the only one in Derbyshire. Near the Fluor Spar Mine is a Mountain one face of which is open and quite perpendicular so that all the strata may be seen. This is called Mam Tor or the Shivering Mountain on account of the portions of Earth and Stones which are frequently falling from this side. The strata are not large and a great part consists of Rotten Stone which is so much used to Polish Metals etc. The chief substance at Castleton appears to be the brownish sparry limestone which at least at the Peak is not bituminous. I did not see any Toadstone and was told that little was found. There are also some Mines of Calamine near Castleton. There is but one Inn (and that a very bad one) at which Post Chaises are to be had—this is called the Castle Inn. Castleton is probably a corruption of Castletown. Nearby over the Peak are some remains apparently of a Castle.

At about 7 o'clock in the evening we set out for Sheffield—at about 1½ or 2 miles from C we went up a hill about 2 Miles in length—arrived at Sheffield 16 Miles by 11 o'clock PM. Went to the Tontine Inn one of the best and largest in England.

SATURDAY JUNE 11TH Sheffield is a large Town, not Handsome nor regularly built—it is in a valley and the country about it is fine and diversified with Hills and Dales. In the morning called on Mr. Curr the colliery Agent for the Duke of Norfolk and delivered him a letter from Dr. McNab. Mr. Curr a very hospitable and civil man and appears to be an able mechanic.

	£	s	d
Bill at Castleton	£1	6	6
Expences at the Mines	0	12	0
Post to Sheffield 16 M	0	18	8
Driver	0	2	10
Turnpikes	0	1	0
	£3	1	0

SUNDAY JUNE 12TH   Dined with Mr. Curr.

MONDAY JUNE 13TH   Mr. Curr breakfasted with us, after which we went to one of the four collieries belonging to the Duke of Norfolk. This one is called Sheffield Park Colliery and is situated in the Town towards the South East. The works are also carried on in the same direction (i.e. South East) under a hill. There is a level or opening by which persons may enter this work on foot but we were (to save time and trouble) taken to the mouth of the shaft by which the coal is drawn up in square wooden vessels bound and cased with iron called Corves. Each of those used at Sheffield hold between 500 and 600 Cwt. (*sic*)

These corves have at the bottom four small Iron Wheels by which they run in the Cast Iron rail roads both above and underground.

By an ingenious machine worked by water and invented by Mr. Curr two of these corves are drawn up and two let down at the same time, by the same machinery a Platform slides over the mouth of the shaft and the two full corves are pushed forward by two empty ones which are next to go down, and the full corves are then rolled by men to the edge of a Platform where by a discharging machine also invented by Mr. Curr they are emptied into carts etc. Each corf is guided by friction rollers during the descent and ascent in the shaft, and as these meet about the middle of the shaft this divides there somewhat in this manner. Mr. Curr and myself in one corf with Mr. Curr's brother and Mr. Savaresi in the other thus descended the shaft which was 25 yards deep in about ½ a minute whilst two corves went up loaded with coal. Upon our arrival at the bottom we found some Boys and a Man who received the empty corves as they came down and hooked on those which were loaded in their room. The loaded corves are brought from the places which are worked for coal (and which are from the bottom of this shaft from 1 mile & ¼ to 1 & ½ mile distant) these corves I say are brought along iron rail roads by a horse guided by a boy, and at every 250 yards, this boy and horse are met by another boy and horse either taking back the empty corves or bringing loaded ones. These boys make an exchange of corves so that each Boy and

Horse goes and returns 250 yards in a stated place like a limited stage. Although each corf weighs about 250 (*sic* MS) cwt and when loaded contains between 5 and 6 cwt of coals yet by Mr. Curr's invention of iron rail roads by the rollers or wheels of the corves and by the passages being nearly perfectly level, one Horse is able to draw without difficulty from 12 to 14 loaded corves at one time, whereas before the Iron rail roads were used only two corves could be drawn at once. By this means 200 Tons of coals have been raised at this colliery in one day by the aid of 9 horses, and the machine above ground above mentioned. The corves are fixed one behind another by means of a Hook and Chain. As they at present are not full of work they only raise 150 Tons per Day. The places where the corves meet and exchange horses and drivers are called Pass By's because in these places only the corves can pass each other.

After we had walked a small distance from the bottom of the shaft we each got into a corf which being linked with others were drawn forwards in the manner already mentioned thro the passages which were just wide enough to receive the rail road for the corves and were thus transferred at the different Pass By's (to the number of nine) till we arrived at the working places about 1 mile and ¼ from the shaft from whence we had started. The height of these passages is about 5 feet and a half or near 6 feet. The roof in generall was dark grey schiefer Thon called here blue bind and the sides sometimes of the same, and sometimes of coal occasionally strengthened both sides and roof with upright Pieces and cross Rafters of wood. When the roof was coal it was always of that hard sort here called Branch about 6 inches thick which is on the upper part of the main Stratum, Bed or Seam of coal, and which (when the coal is worked out) is always left to strengthen the roof. The main stratum of coal in this mine is about 6 feet thick but has near the middle in general about 12 or 13 inches of a light coloured clay. Air shafts are sunk every ½ mile nearly and two are worked at a time, a fire being made at the bottom of one to keep up a current of air. Near the Working Place was a continuation of a passage into which we were cautioned no to go with candles as the fire Damp was there for want of a proper circulation. In the working places when they have removed a certain portion for 20 yards or more of the face of the seam of coals, they support the open part behind them with Punches or Props of timber which as they advance they remove and the incumbent strata gradually fall in and fill up the space. This can only be done when the Roof is brittle and not too strong (the stratum of coal dips about 3 and ½ inches in a yard). When otherwise they can only cut away 6 or 8 yards of coal and then leave 8 yards as a support alternatively as at Newcastle. The coal is dug out with picks and is in general in large Fragments; these sell at Sheffield at 3 pence farthing per Cwt. The getters of coal work about 8 hours per day (i.e. from 3 AM till 11). From the summit of the hill to the Level is about 150 yards. 2 Common Steam Engines to draw off the water.

From hence we went to Attercliffe another colliery of the Duke of Norfolk about 2 miles to East of Sheffield on the Rotherham road. This is about 100 yards deep in the Shaft. The other matters are much the same as at Sheffield Park excepting that a small steam engine as at Coal Brook Dale works Mr. Curr's machine for drawing up the corves which here are only two instead of four as at Sheffield Park.

The Strata over these collieries especially at Sheffield Park appear to be a white or yellowish white micaceous grit, White Post, and dark grey schiefer Thon which at Sheffield they call blue Bind. This sort of Grit with dark grey or blue Argills Schistus and the above mentioned Schiefer Thon appear to constitute the strata of the hills etc. around Sheffield.

Dined with Mr. Curr.

TUESDAY JUNE 14TH   In the morning we went with Mr. Curr to see a Steel Work (or where the Iron is converted into the blister'd Bar Steel) belonging to a Mr. Marshall. The form of these furnaces is like the annexed sketch and the height with the chimney etc. perhaps 30 or 40 feet. [*opposite*]

The Bars are of various sizes and are about 12 feet long—they are placed horizontally in the chest so as not to touch each other on a stratum of powdered charcoal and between each layer of Bars a stratum of the charcoal is placed, and when the chest is thus filled, the whole is covered with a stratum of charcoal and this again well covered with Sand to prevent the combustion of the charcoal. The aperture by which the people entered to arrange the Iron is then well closed up and then the fire kindled (the Fuel is Pit coal) and the Red Heat is kept up e.g. from Sunday Eveng till Saturday following. There is a small aperture in the side by which a Bar may be occasionally taken out, and also the degree of heat seen. This forms Blistered

A   The Fire Place
B   The Stone Chest in which the Iron Bars are placed
C   The Vaulted Roof
D   The chimney

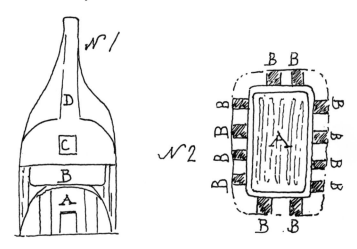

No. 2 is the ground plan, of the Stone Chest or part in which the Iron Bars are placed.
A is the Chest with the Bars.
BB etc. are Flues by which the Flame passes up so as to be reverberated on the top of this chest by means of the Vaulted Roof, C in No. 1.

Bar Steel (NB here about 6 Tons are made in each Furnace. The Blisters are hollow). To form what is called German Steel the Blistered Bar Steel is forged under Hammers and reduced even occasionally (as for watchmakers etc.) to the size of $\frac{1}{8}$ of an inch square. NB Mr. Huntsman at Attercliffe[1] near Sheffield is celebrated for the steel which he makes.

Dined at the Ordinary and met Mr. Joseph Walker and gave him Mr. Winter's letter. In the evening went to Rotherham 6 miles.

[1] Benjamin Huntsman (1704-1776), clockmaker, who in search for a better spring steel discovered the crucible method of making cast steel. Walker of Grenoside is said to have got knowledge of Huntsman's method by doubtful means and adapted it in his own steel works.

Sheffield has many Manufactories for Silver Plate etc. and is well known as the place where a great part of the Cutlery used in England (as well as exported) is made. The Tontine Inn at Sheffield is one of the largest and best in England.

Bill at Sheffield etc.	£2	16	0
Dinner at Ordinary	0	12	0
Post to Rotherham 6 miles	0	7	0
Driver	0	1	6
Turnpike	0	0	9
half £1 18 6	£3	17	3

The road from Sheffield to Rotherham is very good and the country fine. Grit stone prevailed all the way. The Grit Stone here and at Sheffield is white or yellowish white with Ochry zones or veins —that at Sheffield is the whitest and has some mica mixed with it and nodules of quartz of an in. or more often appear in it.

WEDNESDAY JUNE 15TH Went to breakfast with Mr. Joseph Walker who resides in an elegant house about ½ Mile from Rotherham on the Doncaster road—after breakfast Mr. Walker desired a Mr. Yates one of the superintendants to show us the works—at least those in and near Rotherham.

At about ¾ of a Mile from the Town at Masbro' is the foundery where they cast cannon of all sizes. The process is the same nearly as at Coalbrook Dale but the Models or those which are used to imprint the Figure of the different parts of the cannon in the sand are hollow and of cast iron whereas those at C. B. Dale are solid and are of wood. The cannon here is divided into six pieces including the head which is afterwards cut off.

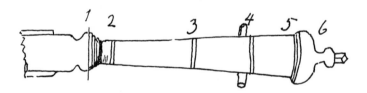

Two moulds properly fitted up are placed in the Pit, and one is cast at about 11 in the morning and the other at 4 in the afternoon. The

Turning and Boring Machines are worked by a water wheel. The Turning is performed by square pieces of hardened steel forced close to the sides with wedges or screws. The pieces of steel are about 2 inches square and 4 inches long. For the Mouldings etc. the tools are made of a proper figure. The Boring Machine is simpler and better constructed than that at Coalbrook Dale—the machine to cut the heads is also better—it acts like a chizzle. The cannon here are cast sometimes from the Blast Furnaces and sometimes from the Wind Furnaces in which they melt the Pig Iron as well as old cannon etc. which they break by letting them fall one on the other from a great height. The Blast Furnaces are about 40 or 46 feet high and 11 feet wide where the bases of the two cones meet. The fuel is coak. The Ore is got about 2 miles from Rotherham; it is the Thonartiger Eisenstein of a pale brown or grey colour and is much intermixed with Calc: Spar and contains shells etc. The best is in nodules, the worst appears rather schistose. Occasionally this is mixed with a certain proportion of red Ruddle and Hematites from Lancashire or Cumberland.

The Iron used to make the Tin Plate is thus mixed and is fused with charcoal instead of coak in a Blast Furnace 30 feet high by 10 feet in width. When this sort of Iron is reduced to plates sufficiently thin the plates are scoured with sand and water acidulated with Vinegar—they are then dipped into melted Tin covered with a mixture of Resin and Fish Oil—the plates are repeatedly dipped till they have acquired a proper thickness of Tin on their surface. In other places they cast all sorts of Pots, Iron Rails, Cylinders and every sort of cast iron utensils.

In another part at some distance we visited the forges which are as usual worked by water wheels (here undershot). The Iron which is forged into the best bars is first heated in a charcoal forge and reduced to a certain size under the Hammer. It is then heated in a forge with Pit coal and is then wrought into a Bar of a proper size. We afterwards visited the Rolling and Slitting Mills which are as usual. In the Blast Furnace they use cylinders to blow—the Pistons are worked by a water wheel and are so contrived as to force Air into two wind chests both by the rise and fall of each Piston so that 4 stroakes are produced in the time usually required for two. Messrs. Walkers in all their works employ about 800 Men; they Manufacture all sorts of the common Ironmongery Goods—see account of the Steel Works in the next Book. After dinner set out for Doncaster 12 M a fine road and beautiful country. The Grit Stone prevailed till about 4 or 4 and ½ miles from Rotherham at which distance Limestone appeared and some quarries of it were seen near the 5 and 6 Mile Stone going from R. Rotherham is not a large Town, neither does it appear to contain anything remarkable. This limestone is used by Messrs. Walker in their Founderies.

In another quarter we went to see the Steel Works belonging to Mr. Booth. a partner with Messrs. Walkers. These works are very considerable. The Furnaces in which the Iron is converted into steel are many but in general they work two at a time—each of these contain about 8 Tons of Iron Bars 10 feet in length—these Furnaces have two chests (those at Sheffield had but one) and the flame passes up the middle between them. The other parts of the operation are the same as at Sheffield. Near these are the Furnaces for making the cast steel as at Sheffield—the Cast Steel is prepared from the Blistered Bar Steel which is broken into small pieces and also from scrap steel, old knife blades etc. These are melted in wind Furnaces, the fire places of which are horizontal and on a level with the Pavement (the Fuel is Pit coal)—the Pots or Crucibles are in this form rather long and have very little Plumbago in their composition. Each crucible will commonly serve about a day (each Melting requires about 3 hours). The melted steel is then poured into cast iron moulds in two parts which join with a rabbit. In these according to the size they cast bars from 16 to 40 lb. The Bars are then heated and forged into smaller and longer Bars of various sizes.

N.B. In the Iron Forges the Scrap Iron is piled upon round earthen Bottoms about 10 inches in Diameter, these are then heated in a welding heat, the earthen Bottom then drops off and the Mass of Iron is worked under the Hammers.

	£	s	d
Bill at Rotherham	£0	17	6
Post to Doncaster 12 miles	0	14	0
Driver	0	2	0
Turnpikes	0	1	6
half £0 17 6	£1	15	0

THURSDAY JUNE 16TH Doncaster is a large Town with some handsome buildings. The country about it is fine. Set out at ½ past 10 o'Clock AM—fine road and country; at about 6 miles from Doncaster the Limestone appeared in some places near the 7 Mile Stone covered with a pale greyish white indurated schistose Argillaceous Marle—in other parts on the road Limestone appeared covered with yellowish and white grit. Arrived in Ferrybridge, a small Town 15 Miles from Doncaster—the Angel an excellent Inn. From Ferrybridge went to Tadcaster 12 Miles—a small Town. N.B. Limestone began to appear about 4 or 5 Miles from Rotherham and continued to be seen in various places as far and even beyond Tadcaster—it probably extends to York. From Tadcaster we proceeded to York 9 Miles. York is a large City situate in a plain—the country is fine—the Cathedral is one of the finest Gothic Edifices now remaining in England. Here Constantius the son of Constantine the Great is supposed to be interred and his effegy in stone (very ancient) is shewn. N.B. the Limestone above mentioned was often covered by a hard schistose marle of the Argillaceous sort, the colour greyish white—slightly effervesces.

FRIDAY JUNE 17TH Set out from York and went to Easingwold 13 Miles from thence to North Allerton 19 M through Thirsk. These three towns are not very considerable the country is fine and the roads excellent. At about 4 Miles from Easingwold the road is repaired with a grey stone which in the external parts was ochry or yellow to the depth of 2 inches or more. It appears to be a compact grit contains small particles of Mica and effervesces briskly. It gives some few sparks with a steel. The Postillion said it was Whin Stone and was found in great plenty in the neighbourhood (is it the true whin stone?). From North Allerton we went to Darlington 16 Miles also a small town and from Darlington to Durham 18 Miles—near Darlington they dig and burn a hard yellow schistose marle which they call limestone—it makes bad lime, but certainly does not contain a large quantity of Calcareous Earth as it does not effervesce till scraped into a powder. This substance extends to Durham and also to Sunderland. The road from Darlington to Durham is rather hilly but from Rotherham to York and almost to Darlington it is nearly level. Durham is a pretty large city, part of which is on a hill. The river Wear runs thro' it to Sunderland. The Cathedral in respect to Architecture is for a great part Saxon, the rest is Gothic and altho' it has undergone considerable repairs they (very properly) have not altered the original stile. The Organ is a very good one.

SATURDAY JUNE 18TH Set out from Durham and proceeeded to Sunderland 13 M. The road very good and fine country. The yellow indurated schistose Marle (already mentioned) is here burned for lime as at Darlington.

Sunderland is a very large sea Port Town much more considerable than Durham in extent and in population. The River Wear flows through the Town and empties itself into the Sea. The most remarkable thing at Sunderland is the Iron Bridge which is now nearly finished. This Bridge will be completed by next September (exactly 3 years from the beginning of it). Mr. Burdon one of the Members for the County of Durham erects it at his sole expence, and invented the Blocks which are the essential parts of its construction. The expence will be 20 or £25,000. Mr. Wilson an Architect of Sunderland has had the management of the whole—the Bridge is in this form.

At each end are Stone Warehouses and the Bridge is formed of Cast Iron Blocks which are made to join end to end. Along the sides AA. Bars of wrought Iron an inch thick and 3 broad are let in and cover the joints. These are fastened with bolts and nuts which pass through. The width of the River here is 236 feet which consequently is the span of the Arch of the Bridge. The height of the Arch at low water is 100 feet, and as the Water rises

10 feet the height at all times is 90 feet so that Vessels such as Colliers etc. may pass without lowering their Top Sails. Dined at the Bridge Inn and drank tea with Mr. Wilson. In the evening set out

and arrived at Newcastle upon Tyne 14 Miles. The road not very good. Crossed the Wear in a Ferry Boat. At about 5 Miles from Newcastle found the road repaired with greyish white Micaceous Grit. Went to the Queens Head in Pilgrim Street.

SUNDAY JUNE 19TH   Called on Mr. Chambers the Mayor and left Mr. Joseph Walker's letter.

MONDAY JUNE 20TH   Went with Mr. Chambers to see the Rooms of the Literary & Philosophical Society of Newcastle—the chief part of their collection consists of the Strata of the Coal Mines and of the varieties of coal found in the vicinity of Newcastle; also some good Spathose Lead Ores and crystals of Galena from Cumberland. Went afterwards to see the Assembly Rooms which are very Elegant and Neat. Afterwards went with Mr. Chambers to dine about 2 miles out of Town with Mr. Hood the Sheriff. Supped with Mr. Chambers at the Mansion House.

TUESDAY JUNE 21ST   Went to see the Lead Works belonging to Messrs. Walker and Fishwick to whom I had a letter from Mr. Jos. Walker. In these works they roll sheet lead, make Shot, Minium and Ceruse. The Sheet lead is first cast into Plates about 4 feet square and 3 inches thick. These are afterwards placed on a long table which is traversed by a series of wooden rollers in the middle of which a pair of cast iron large rollers are fixed between which the lead is passed— as it extends it slips over the length of the table by means of the Wooden Rollers. It is thus repeatedly passed backwards and 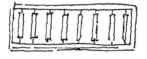 forwards the Rollers of iron being each time more and more approached till it is sufficiently thin and extended.

The Minium is prepared by melting Lead in a large Reverberating Furnace. The flame passes up on each side and plays over the surface of the Metal contained in a square shallow wide Trough or Chest of Stone. The Fuel is made underneath. The first produce is the yellowish oxide called Massicot—this is subjected to a second operation of the same kind and then is brought into the state of Minium. They do not here make Litharge.

To make the Ceruse the lead is cast into thin grates each of which weighs about 2 lb. Each mould contains 6 of these grates so that 12 lb are cast nearly at once. In certain buildings for  the purpose they place on the floor a stratum of Horse Dung (or Tanners Bark for which Messrs. Walkers have a Patent). They then place Earthen Pots which hold each about a quart so as entirely to cover this stratum of Dung or Bark and in some measure to be buried part of their depth in it. Over these Pots filled with vinegar they place about 6 or 8 of these thin Leaden Grates—they then place some rows of the Pots turned bottom upwards and on these they lay another floor of Planks, afterwards dung, pots with vinegar and Leaden Grates. Thus they go on till the whole chamber is filled and the top is covered with Planks and Dung. In about two months they open these beds and find the lead in the state of Ceruse, most commonly throughout. If any Lead remains in the state of Metal it is separated and cast over again. The Ceruse is ground in Mills with water and is then dryed in earthen pans—formerly the Ceruse was ground dry by which the People employed suffered much in Health. The present mode was invented by one of the Partners Mr. Ward who had the Golden Medal of the Socy of Arts given him in consequence. The Mills which grind the Ceruse are worked by a Steam Engine on Boulton's construction; the Rolling Mill is worked by a Common Engine.

The Shot is made in the usual way by letting lead melted with Orpiment pass thro' Iron Vessels like cullendars into water—the shot is then polished in a Barrel turned with a handle.

Dined and supped with Mr. Chambers.

WEDNESDAY JUNE 22ND   Called on Mr. Johnston at Byker and left Dr. McNabb's letter—dined with Mr. Chambers—in the eveng went to the Play.

THURSDAY JUNE 23RD   Breakfasted with Mr. Johnston at Byker, afterwards went with him and his son to Heaton Colliery. The shaft here is divided into three parts; the coal is drawn by two of these divisions and the third is for the Engine Rods. The coal here is of a good quality. The Strata here (as indeed all over this country) is white and brown Micaceous Grit and Schiefer Thon blue grey or black. The coal is here raised in Basket Corves which contain 24 Pecks. The coal is conveyed to the water side by what they here call Waggons made of wood with small iron wheels which have a Rabbit which fit the wooden rail roads. The Basket Corves are fastened by a spring Woodcock eye Hook to the Rope by which it is raised from the Pit. There are two of these ropes in each Pit one of which rises when the other descends. The corf which is raised is immediately discharged by a man at the mouth of the Pit. As soon as he has placed it on a small sledge drawn by a Horse he then fastens an empty corf to the hook and casts it into the Pit.

The waggons can contain about 8 Corves or 5300 lb. The Ropes are worked by a steam engine, common construction, the cylinder of which is 70 inches in diameter. The same raises the water out of the mine, 300 gallons at each stroke. The High Main Coal at Heaton is about 85 fathoms deep they have not yet reached the Low Main Coal which everywhere is 65 fathoms below the High Main Coal which prove that the same strata extend all over the country about Newcastle, and that the different depth at which the High Main coal is found, is occasioned by the undulation of the Superincumbent Strata or their diversity in thickness and numbers. The coal in general here dips to the SE one yard in 20. At some of the Collieries they can raise 600 Tons per day but they employ more Horses than at Sheffield (from 80 to 100 in a colliery). From Heaton we went to Biggar's Main Colliery which is very extensive. but so much incommoded with the Fire Damp that in many places they are obliged to use Steel Mills and Flints instead of candles—even these sometimes cause explosions. All the collieries about Newcastle are very liable to Fire Damps, much more than at Sheffield, which is one reason why they work the mines in a different manner—at Newcastle the coal is worked out so as to leave square apartments of about 6 yards, between each of which they leave a Pillar of coal about 8 yards square. Some of the collieries can go 4 Miles underground—Dined with Mr. Geo. Losh[1] at Saltwell Side about 3 Miles from Newcastle. Promised to send my Paper to his Brother Mr. John Losh Woodside near Carlisle.

FRIDAY JUNE 24TH   Dined with Mr. Johnston at Byker. N.B. to send to his son Kirwen and Babington's tables.

SATURDAY JUNE 25TH   Went with Mr. Geo. Losh to Lemington about 4 miles to NW of Newcastle on the road found a dark grey stone with crystals of white feldtspar—it appears to be a species of Trapp Porphyry. It is here called Whag Stone, perhaps by Whag they also understand Whin. The whin stone of Newcastle is evidently a species of hard micaceous Grit or Sand Stone and is only a modification of the other variety which they call Post. The Blue Whag Stone forms a considerable Dyke or Heave. Near Lemington we called on Lord Dundonald who now with Messrs. Losh is separating Sal: Soda from Sea Salt and also is about a new process to make white lead. The mode of preparing the Soda according to the account which Lord Dundonald gave me is as follows—Solutions of Sea Salt and of Vitriol of Iron are mixed together, and then a quantity of clay is added so as to absorb the whole. This is then dried and exposed to a strong heat in a Reverberating Furnace. By this means the Muriatic and Sulphuric Acids change their bases so that Muriate of Iron and Sulphate of Soda or Glaubers Salt are formed. The Sulphate of Soda is then separated by elixiviation and is crystallized by evaporation. It is then mixed with charcoal and being exposed to heat a Hepar Sulph: is formed—this is dissolved evaporated and then exposed to a strong heat so as to drive off the Sulphur. I have some doubts about the success of this operation.

Dined and supped with Mr. Chambers.

---

[1] One of the family of Losh, of importance in the chemical, engineering and coal industries on Tyneside. In 1794 John Losh joined in a partnership with Lord Dundonald in the chemical works visited by Hatchett at Bell's Close. His brother William later brought from Paris the Le Blanc process of soda manufacture and this was used at the new works at Walker. In 1809 the Losh, Wilson and Bell partnership, ironfounders and engineers, was formed and William Losh was one of the financial supporters of George Stephenson in his locomotive experiments. He was a joint patentee with Stephenson in the lap-joint rail. George Losh had an interest in Walker Colliery where salt springs were tapped for the chemical works.

SUNDAY JUNE 26TH   At 7 o'clock on Sunday morning I set out in the Berwick and Edinburgh Coach. Breakfasted at Morpeth 14½ Miles from Newcastle—a good road and fine country. Morpeth a pretty considerable Town—from M went to Alnwick 19½ or 20 Miles. Alnwick is not quite so large as Morpeth. Went to see Alnwick Castle the seat of the D of Northumberland—not much of the Antient part remains except the walls and a Saxon entrance. Dined at Alnwick—set out at ½ past 2 at about 1 mile from A is a stone cross erected on the spot where Malcolm King of Scotland was killed. Arrived at Belford a small Town 15 Miles from Alnwick. From Morpeth to this place I observed that the road was repaired with a dark grey hard stone which became ochry on the surface and appeared to be the Scots Whin stone—from Belford proceeded to Berwick 15 Miles. The roads here were made of Whin stone and Limestone—the country is beautiful and all the way commands a fine view of the Sea. Arrived at Berwick in the eveng at 8 o'clock. Berwick is situated on the Tweed which when the Tide is in is broad. On entering B. we passed a stone Bridge of 15 Arches. The Town is regularly fortified (I believe by Cromwell) it is not handsome and the pavement is very bad—it is chiefly remarkable for the Salmon which is catched in the Tweed and is either dried, spiced, pickled or sent fresh to London.

MONDAY JUNE 27TH   remained at Berwick.

TUESDAY JUNE 28TH   Set out in the Edinburgh coach at 9 o'clock AM. Changed horses at Pressy Inn and proceeded to Dunbar [1] miles from Berwick. Dunbar is a moderate sized Town on the sea shore. The country about it is fine and well cultivated. Dunbar is 28 miles from Berwick. From Dunbar we went to Haddington 10 miles a small Town situate in a fine country. From Haddington we proceeded through a fine country chiefly near the Sea Shore—in passing we left Preston Pans on our right and at 8 arrived at Edinburgh.

WEDNESDAY JUNE 29TH   In the morning Mr. Savaresi and Dr. Morelli[2] breakfasted with me—afterwards called on Dr. Hope[3] who

---

1 blank in MS.
2 Dr. Morelli was probably a friend of Dr. Savaresi on a visit to Edinburgh.
3 Dr. Thomas Charles Hope (1766-1844) followed Joseph Black in the Chair of Chemistry at Edinburgh in 1785. He was the discoverer of Strontium and had Huttonian views on geology.

is the Assistant to Dr. Black[1]. With Dr. Hope we called on Dr. Black, a thin old man but pleasant in his manners—dined with Mr. Savaresi at Pooles Coffee House—called on Mrs. Walker, Dr. Crichton's sister in Queen Street and in the eveng walked with Mr. Savaresi & Dr. Morelli to Leith.

THURSDAY JUNE 30TH   In the morning went with Dr. Hope to Salisbury Craggs which are about $\frac{1}{4}$ of a Mile to SE by S of the city. These as well as most of the Hills in the neighbourhood are composed of the Scots whin stone and Grit. Dined with Mr. Savaresi at the Coffee House; in the eveng called on Mr. Ramsey at Leith.

FRIDAY JULY 1ST   In the fore noon went with Mr. Savaresi and Dr. Morelli to see the University. The Anatomical Theatre is in the new building and appears too large for the purpose as the Students in the Gallery cannot see the preparations and dissections with any degree of accuracy—there are upon the average between 5 and 600 Medical Students. There are two terms in the year in each of which about 20 students take the degree of Doctor of Medicine. The Anatomical collection does not appear to be well arranged and the wax preparations are shamefully neglected so that many are spoiling and many are spoiled. Went to hear Dr. Coventry's[2] lecture on Agriculture but what with the reverberation of the room, the quickness of utterance and the low voice of the lecturer I did not hear above one word in three. Dined with Dr. Duncan Professor of Medicine[3]; the company consisted chiefly of young students who sat silent like boys before their master.

SATURDAY JULY 2ND   Mr. Savaresi set out this Morning at 2 o'clock and returned by the Newcastle coach to Newcastle, thro' a mistake of his Landlord. At 9 o'clock I accompanied Dr. Morelli to Breakfast with Mr. Benj. Bell the Author of the celebrated Treatise on Gun Shot Wounds and other similar works. He is a man of simple and unaffected manners perfectly well bred and entertaining in con-

[1] Dr. Joseph Black (1728-1799) Professor of Chemistry at Glasgow from 1766 to 1795, a friend and encourager of James Watt.
[2] Dr. Andrew Coventry M.D. (1764-1832) was the first Professor of Agriculture at Edinburgh from 1790-1831.
[3] Dr. Andrew Duncan (1744-1828) was Professor of Institutes of Medicine or Physiology at Edinburgh 1789-1819. Founder of the Royal Public Dispensary, the Edinburgh Lunatic Asylum and the Caledonian Horticultural Society.

versation. At 1 o'clock went with Mr. Ramsey and Dr. Morelli to see the Edinburgh Volunteers reviewed by Ld Adam Gordon in the Meadows near the City. The Corps consists of between 5 & 600 or nearly 600 Men mostly Gentlemen including several Professors etc, they made a very respectable appearance and went well in general thro' the different evolutions. Dined with the Capt. of the Grenadiers of this Corps (Mr. Kerr in Georges Square) a friend of Major Crichton. In the evening went to the Play and saw Miss Wallis perform in Every one has his faults and the Sultan.

SUNDAY JULY 3RD   Wrote to Rackett—called on Dr. Hope and dined with Mr. Ramsey of Leith.

MONDAY JULY 4TH   Paid a visit to Dr. Walker Professor of Nat: History[1] to whom I had a letter from Dr. Wavell of Barnstaple. Dr. Walker is a pleasant elderly man and when I drank tea with him in the evening offered me any service in respect to my intended Tour to the Western Islands which he had formerly visited during 9 months. After tea I accompanied him to the meeting of the Royal Society of Edinburgh when he proposed me as a member. Supped at home with Dr. Morelli.

TUESDAY JULY 5TH   Accompanied Dr. Hope to a Whin Stone quarry called Bells Mills at about 1 Mile to the west of Edinburgh. The Whin Stone here forms a considerable Bed, over and under which are the strata of Blackish Argillaceous Schistus which is more indurated in those parts which are in immediate contact with the Whin Stone— this is one of the facts adduced in favour of Dr. Hutton's Theory— another is at Salisbury Craggs where the Whin Stone appears to have surrounded certain detached masses of the sandstone which some times is upon and at other times under the whin. A third fact is pointed out in the bed of a rivulet not far from Bells Mills where the whin in two places intersects the Argillaceous Schistus which forms the bed of the river so as to cross it (like the remains of a Bridge) nearly East and West. Near the rivulet is a sulphurous or Hepatic Spring over which is a neat Temple built by Ld. Gardenstone? Went

[1] Dr. John Walker, D.D. (1731-1803) Professor of Natural History at Edinburgh from 1779-1803. Moderator of the General Assembly of the Church of Scotland in 1790. *An economical history of the Hebrides and Highlands of Scotland*, was published posthumously in 1808, Edinburgh, 2 vols.

to hear Dr. Walkers Lecture on Mineralogy. Dined with Lord Methven in St. Andrews Square. Supped with Mr. Feild.

WEDNESDAY JULY 6TH   Received a visit from Dr. Rotherham Professor of Chemistry at St. Andrews—Mr. Martin a very ingenious Portrait Painter accompanied him—Went to Dr. Walkers Lecture. Dined at home.

THURSDAY JULY 7TH   Mr. Thompson a gentleman introduced to me by Mr. Feild breakfasted with me. Afterwards we went to Calton Hill on which the Observatory is built. Calton Hill is just without the City to the East or on the side towards Leith. It is principally composed (especially the upper part of it) of a species of whin or Trapp Porphyry which with the Feldtspar frequently contains Calc: Spar. Other parts of it between or rather below the Porphyry are composed, first of a dark brown soft Argillaceous Grit, and under this often a species of Mandelstein or rather a Breccia or Puddingstone. In these substances a pale reddish yellow crystallized substance is often found which by some is considered as a decomposed Feldtspar but the Figure is more like some of the Zeolites found at Sky. In other parts of these substances a black brittle shining apparently Bituminous substance is often found which however is not inflamable and does not melt in the flame of a candle; it may perhaps be a species of variety of coal Blende.

   Dined at home—supped with Dr. Walker in company with a Mr. Keith, Mr. Creech & Mr. Robert Jameson of Sheriff Brea at Leith.

FRIDAY JULY 8TH   After Breakfast went with Messrs. Jameson [1] and Thompson [2] to visit the Pentland Hills which are about 5 miles to the West of Edinburgh. These or at least that which we examined appear to be composed of varieties of whitish and pale red Argillaceous Grit which passes into different degrees of induration becoming finer in grain and at length part becoming a sort of Hornstone or Petro Silex which by some has been taken for compact Feldtspar. I

[1] Mr. Robert Jameson (1774-1854) mineralogist and geologist followed Walker as Professor of Natural History at Edinburgh in 1804. He was a Wernerian geologist.
[2] Mr. Thomas Thomson (1773-1852) became Professor of Chemistry at Glasgow University 1818-1846.

also found some portions of Breccias and Mandelsteins containing nodules of Agates etc. in a sort of Wacke but the principal substance appeared to me to be the varieties of the above mentioned Grit. Dined at home.

SATURDAY JULY 9TH   Breakfasted at home. Dined with Mr. Jameson at Leith in company with Dr. Rotherham Mr. Thompson Mr. Creech and Mr. Sheriff of Leith.

SUNDAY JULY 10TH   After breakfast went with Mr. Jameson to the Museum to see the collection of Minerals.

This collection is not well arranged and is named after the fanciful Nomenclature of Dr. Walker which he has chiefly formed from Pliny and other Antient Authors whose descriptions are vague and unintelligible. The most valuable part of the collection is that of the Swedish Minerals the best part of which were sent to him, Dr. Walker, by Baron Alstroemer the friend of Linneus. The specimens of Spathose Lead from the Lead Hills are very fine and also those of the Siliceous Zinc Ore from Wanlock Head. In Mr. Robert Jameson's collection which I saw on Saturday is a fine specimen of the Staurolite from Strontian with cross crystals like that of Andreasberg in the Hartz[1]. Also a green substance resembling Olivine in everything but Hardness in a sort of whin stone from[2]   .

Prehnite resembling that from Dauphine but in colour like that of the Cape of Good Hope from Arthurs Seat—also red Zeolite like that of Adelfors from Shetland.

OBSERVATIONS ON THE WHIN STONE

This substance prevails much about Edinburgh and according to Dr. Hutton is the predominant stone in Scotland. It appears to be a mixed stone composed of Argill, Quartz, Hornblende and sometimes Calcareous Earth or Calc: Spar—it varies much in colour, grain and structure—certain varieties of it are of a dark grey and of a fine close grain so much as to resemble Trapp. Others again have the Hornblende in distinct crystalline portions and the quartz in distinct small masses. It often contains nodules of Calc: Spar and Zeolites as at Salisbury Craggs. The Calc: Spar and also Feldtspar often forms Veins in it. It often passes into a species of Porphyry as at Calton Hill and also into a Mandelstein as at Salisbury Craggs. Sometimes part

1 This mineral is Harmotome.
2 blank in MS.

appears as a Breccia as at Calton Hill. In many places it has above or below it strata of Sandstone or Grit as at Salisbury Craggs. It does not appear to form strata but on the contrary Solid Beds which either are upon the Sandstone as at Salisbury Craggs or upon Argillaceous Schistus as at Bells Mills or at the Quarry adjacent. The Beds of Whin Stone every where appear to have vertical fissures and at Salisbury Craggs or that part in the vicinity called Arthurs Seat it assumes the figure in great measure of Basaltes and breaks into Polygonal Prisms or Columns.

The interruptions and breaks it produces with the sandstone at Salisbury Craggs and with the Argillaceous Schistus at Bells Mills are those which Dr. Hutton supposes to be very corroborative of his Theory—he also draws inferences from the Pentland Hills particularly from the supposed existence of compact Feldtspar, which to me does not appear to be such but only various degrees in the induration of the Grit or Sandstone.

It is remarkable that Allan Ramsey has placed the scene of his Gentle Shepherd among these Pentland Hills. In a part of Arthurs Seat I observed in company with Messrs. Thompson and Jameson that the whin formed Strata from one inch to 2 in thickness. Prehnite is also found in Arthurs Seat in the fragments of the columns.

Near or over Arthurs Seat are some Quarries of Sandstone which has a green Argillaceous substance interposed between the strata.

MONDAY JULY 11TH Went with Mr. Rt. Jameson to see the Castle Hill—this is a Whin stone of a Dark Grey and of a close grain resembling Trapp—the fissures are vertical and approach to a columnar figure. The Castle is not at present allowed to be seen.

In the evening called on Dr. Walker and with him and Mr. Jameson visited Holyrood House. The North Wing or Bastion is the part which contains the old apartments of Queen Mary. The chamber in which Rizzio was killed and what are supposed to be marks of his blood are shown. Some chairs etc. worked by Queen Mary and some armour etc. of Lord Darnley. The rest of the Building is a Quadrangle built by Charles 2nd which upon the whole is not unhandsome.

TUESDAY JULY 12TH Visited Arthurs Seat with Messrs. Thompson and Jameson hard Limestone of a red colour formerly found there.

Dr. Morelli sup'd with me. Edinburgh is bounded on the N by the Firth of Forth on the East by Calton Hill west by the Castle Hill and Leith is to the North East. The New Town is handsome particularly Queen Street, Princess Street and St. Andrews Square.

WEDNESDAY JULY 13TH   Set out with Mr. Jameson from Edin'h. at ½ past 10 o'clock, road good and country well cultivated arrived at Linlithgow a small Town not handsome. 16 M. changed chaise & horse; went to Falkirk 8 M—dined—went to Carron to see Iron Works. They say they employ 1000 Men but I do not believe it. They have 5 blast furnaces 36 feet by 18 each make from 2½ Tons to 3 Tons. Here they cast Cannon, Shells, Shot and all sorts of Iron Kettles etc. The Ore is Argillaceous (not rich) found in the neighbourhood. The coal also—the Limestone is brought from Fyfe. To each Blast Furnace they have 4 Cylinders. They cast twice in 24 hours. *Not* equal to Mr. Walkers Works. They do not allow the boring of the cannon to be seen. Make coke on the spot—only use the Ore of the country.

Stirling a pretty large Town situate in a fine well wooded country, much Hill & Dale. The Castle is on a rock much like that at Edinburgh—has a Basaltic appearance, but upon a near inspection appears to be vertical fissures which by transverse divisions appear like the articulated Basalts. The substance is Whin Stone—on the N East face part is decomposed to an ochry brown stone which by decomposition becomes soft as an Earth. Here I observed great quantities of the round Nodules of Whin stone which decomposed and appeared to exfoliate by concentric coats like the Basalte in Bombs of Mr. Faujas St. Fond. These balls were embedded in a soft ochry earth evidently produced by the above mentioned Whin Stone. The Balls appear to me to have been portions of the columnar parts which by Attrition, Decomposition and Exfoliation have assumed this form. This rock and Castle are to the N of the Town.

To the East of Stirling over the Bridge (which is remarkable for the Battle betw: Edward 1 and David Bruce) is a long hill called Haby's Craggs the perpendicular face of which is towards the Town. The distance is about one or 1 & ½ Mile. The top of this hill appears to be of a formation similar to the Castle Hill but the substance of which it is composed contains more mica. N.B. Below the Whin Stone on the NE face of the Castle Hill is a considerable stratum of blackish Argills Schistus occasionally intermixed with Sandstone.

Behind the Haby's Craggs a long chain of Hills which run nearly in a parallel line with it, i.e. NW and SE—near these a copper mine is said to have been lately found. The Saracens Head at Stirling an excellent Inn.

THURSDAY JULY 14TH   Agreed with Mr. Munro of the Saracens Head at Stirling for the chaise at 16 shillings per day and driver at 2s.

Set out from Stirling at $\frac{1}{4}$ before 11 AM the country about Stirling is fine and much diversified with Hills which have all abrupt and broken faces towards the North West. These same chains of hills as well as the single hills all gradually slope to the SE. On leaving Stirling the country became gradually more hilly with heath and less wood. The road also was rough and stoney. At $\frac{1}{4}$ past 3 we arrived at a village called Auchterarder where we dined in a style much superior to what was promised by the appearance of the place. Here I first saw Horn Spoons, Oaten Cake and Broth made of Cabbage and Barley served at Dinner. Auchterarder is 21 Miles from Stirling. At 5 o'clock set out again—the country was open with Hills at a distance. Part was covered with Broom and Heath but much was well cultivated. Upon the whole the country was superior to that on the other side between Stirling and Auchterarder. The first part of the road was good but the remainder rough till we approached near Perth. Perth is 14 Miles from Auchterarder and 35 from Stirling by this road—there is another which is 39 Miles.

The country about Perth is very fine and beautifully diversified with Hills and Valleys with the Highland Hills at some distance. Perth is situate in a valley on the North side of the Frith of Tay but that of the Forth begins from the Island of May 30 Miles below Leith passes Stirling where it at length becomes a rivulet. Perth is a large well built Town—the Bridge is handsome and has nine arches. Towards the South on the opposite side of the river is at some distance the Hill of Dunsinane on the top of which are the ruins of a castle said to be that of Macbeth. On the opposite side about one Mile below the Bridge to the SE of the Town is Kinnoul Hill which is long and lofty—the abrupt face is towards the N or NW facing the river. The lower part is composed of Whin Stone upon which are thick beds of a hard reddish Wacke full of nodules of green Argill with nodules of Agates (a true Mandelstein). On the road we found much Whin hard and fine grained of a dark grey containing Calc: Spar and a green substance somewhat resembling Olivine—this Whin formed some high banks to the South of the road. Some of the Wacke was penetrated with the green earth.

FRIDAY JULY 15TH   At $\frac{1}{2}$ past 10 o'clock set out from the George (an excellent Inn) the country as we advanced became more hilly and interspersed with morasses where Peat was dug. When we had gone about 10 Miles we entered the Highlands and at 16 Miles arrived at Inver a small village on the river Tay—the country in this place is romantic and beautiful—on approaching to Inver I observed that the Hills on the side (which had been cut through to make the road) were chiefly composed of sand and large rounded Pebbles—the road leading to Inver is very pleasant and is planted with various Trees as Ash, Beech, Lime, Planes, Oaks etc. etc. Near Inver is Birnam Hill on which the celebrated Birnam Wood formerly stood, but at present it is nearly denuded of wood excepting some of a shrubby appearance near the Base. From this Hill that of Dunsinore or Dunsinin may be seen being about 8 miles across the country from each other. Dined and remained the rest of the day at Inver. After dinner we went over in a Ferry boat across the river Tay to visit the D. of Athols seat on the opposite side called Dunkeld. The House does not appear to be remarkable. The ruins of the old church remain in contiguity with the modern kirk. The grounds are romantic and on the top of a lofty Mountain the coutry is seen to a considerable distance. I observed that this Mountain and probably those in the vicinity was composed of Chlorite Schiefer which occasionally passed into Micaceous Schistus as well as into a species of Schistus Tegularis. These were occasionally also mixed with large masses of white fat quartz. On returning from the top of this Mountain I had a specimen of Highland Hospitality, for an old woman had placed at the door of her cottage cheese, oaten cake, whey and milk and seemed to accept with reluctance a shilling which I gave her. The country about Inver & Dunkeld is well cultivated and I here for the first time heard the Peasants conversing in the Erse or Gaelic. It is remarkable that on the Inver side the Gaelic is spoken but on that of Dunkeld the English or what is called Scotch is the usual language.

SATURDAY JULY 16TH   At 10 o'clock set out from Inver—the road was chiefly by the side of the River Tay which passes in a meandering manner through the Strath or Plain of Athol from which the Duke takes his title.

The Plain is very beautiful and on each side are high Mountains which near their bases are well covered with wood; at a few miles from Inver Trees of all sorts especially Ash are numerous, and in many parts the Road was planted on each side with them. The road in general was hilly and stoney. At 4 o'clock we arrived at Kenmore 24 Miles from Inver—this is a small village regularly built consisting of a Church and about 14 houses including the Inn— it is situate on the Eastern extremity of Loch Tay upon a portion of land which runs into the Loch in the manner of a Peninsula—on each side are high Mountains composed of Chlorite and Glimmer Schiefer with large masses of white fat quartz and a sort of reddish coarse Argillaceous Grit. A little to the East of the Inn is Tay Mouth, the seat of the Earl of Breadalbane. N.B. some varieties of the Chlorite Schiefer pass into a species of Lapis Ollaris or Pot Stone— the grounds etc. of Ld. Breadalbanes seat are pleasant and well wooded. The House is by no means handsome at least externally; it is of a corrupt antient Architecture and is covered with white Plaster.

The village of Kenmore is a very melancholy dreary looking place and the bad rainy weather did not contribute to render its appearance more favourable. The Inn was well built (probably by Ld. B.) but the people were not very civil.

SUNDAY JULY 17TH   Set out at 7 o'clock from Kenmore—the road was on the side of Loch Tay and (for as much as the weather would allow me to perceive) was romantic and in many parts beautiful. The long and continued rain had swollen all the rivulets, and Torrents large and small were rushing down from the tops of the Mountains, many of these crossed the road and subjected the carriage to violent jolts which much incommoded me as I was very feverish and unwell with a Bilious complaint.

At about 11 o'clock AM we arrived at Killin $16\frac{3}{4}$ Miles from Kenmore. Killin is a small village pretty neat in its appearance, situated at a small distance beyond the extremity of Loch Tay which is the termination of it reckoning from Kenmore situate on the other extremity. The country about Killin is much more pleasant than that about Kenmore as it is better clothed with trees. The Inn was large and really excellent when the situation was considered. Here we breakfasted and set out again at 1 o'clock PM. We now came into a more wild looking country. High Mountains bare of trees appeared on all sides—the road was very rough, stoney and hilly. Small streams ran across in many places and many cascades and torrents occurred. Some of these were perhaps only temporary being produced by the copious rains. After having travelled thus till $\frac{1}{2}$ past 5 in a continual thick and heavy rain we arrived at Tyn Drum 22 Miles from Killin.

The Inn at which we alighted was situate amidst a number of Mountains destitute of trees and only one small house or rather hut was near it (tho' I was told that at about $\frac{1}{2}$ a Mile distance there was a village of nearly 50). I never in my life saw a more desolate and dreary place not even in the remote parts of Russia or Poland, neither does the climate here afford any compensation for the aspect of the country, for from the elevated situation of it as well as from the other local circumstances the rains are almost perpetual and the Inhabitants by their own acknowledgement seldom are conscious of the comfort of a dry day. Near the Inn are the remains of some Lead Mines belonging to Ld. Breadalbane, but which are not worked. The weather and my Indisposition did not permit me to visit and examine the spot.

[Note re Minerals:
Venus Dione found by Dr. Walker in the Westn. Islands, probably Sky
Cyprea Moneta found by Mr. Jameson in Shetland

1 Box from	Exeter
1 do.	Truro
1 do.	Redruth
1 do.	St. Agnes
1 do.	Bath
1 do.	Matlock
2 Casks	Castleton
1 box	Newcastle
2 do	Edinburgh
2 Casks	Glasgow

1 do. left with Mr. Brown of Derby
1 Slab of Marble left with Mr. Brown of Derby
Minerals left with Mrs. Powell of Sunderland
1 Box from Carlisle
1 Cask from Keswick.]

I observed that from Inver in passing thro' all the following places all or most of the Men wore kilts or Fillibegs and that the greater part of the Women went bare footed—the huts are miserable and appeared to me much inferior to those of the Russians and even to those of the Poles. The Highland huts are about 12 feet long by 6 or 7 in width and not more than 7 or 8 feet high to the Eaves. They are composed of rough stones (for Timber is not to be had) heaped on each other and covered with a rude Thatch—the Door is low and as they seldom have chimneys the exit for the Smoke is by a small window generally opposite to the Door. By all accounts the living of these poor People corresponds with their dwellings for they seldom taste Meat.

Our Inn at Tyn Drum was by no means bad, the provisions were good and plentiful and the Beds were also pretty good. I however experienced here as well as in many other places in the Highlands a very great inconvenience which was the negligence with which they excluded the Air and Rain from their Rooms. Most of the windows had one or more broken panes of glass and I luckily discovered a fracture of this kind in my bed room window at Tyn Drum. The People at this place were not so obliging as those at Killin.

MONDAY JULY 18TH Set out at 10 o'clock AM from Tyn Drum— the road was very hilly and the rain continued during the greatest part of the morning—the appearance of the country was much the same as before till we reached Dalmally (at Dalmally they had had rain for 2 Months) 12 Miles from Tyn Drum. Here the country appeared less barren of Trees and the Inn was very tolerable. Dalmally consists but of a few dispersed cottages besides the Inn. Here we dined and at 4 o'clock set out again. As we advanced the aspect of the country improved and the Trees became more numerous. Part of the road was by the side of a beautiful Lake called Lock Awe with several small Islands in it well covered with wood and on some of these were cottages. The Road continued improving from this place and near the Plantations of the D. of Argyll became very good; passed the Castle of the Duke, and arrived at Inverary by 7 o'clock. The Inn we found to be excellent and it well answered the account of Dr. Johnson who says that it was not only commodious but magnificent.

TUESDAY JULY 19TH The weather continued very bad and I there-fore did not go out—from the Windows of the Inn is a fine View of the Duke's Grounds and also of part of Loch Fyne opposite to the

Inn is a lofty Mountain well cover'd with wood situate in the Duke's grounds. The Town of Inverary is pleasantly situate, the Numbers of Houses is but small, about 15, but are well built and plaistered white.

Inverary Castle the Seat of the Duke of Argyll is a heavy looking Building in the form of a Quadrangle with four round Towers, one being at each corner. The Stone of which it is built is a sort of Lapis Ollaris which abounds in the Neighbourhood, as well as certain Varieties of Hornstone Porphyry & Quartz. Loch Fyne affords plenty of fine Salmon, Herrings and various other fish.

WEDNESDAY JULY 20TH After Breakfast we set out at about 11 o'clock, the Road was good and very pleasant as it went round one of the Branches of Loch Fyne, in this manner without going to any considerable distance from Inverary in a straight line. We proceeded 10 Miles and then arrived at Carrindow a small Village on the opposite Bank of the Loch.

Here we found a very neat and comfortable Inn where we dined. In the neighbourhood of Carrindow I found some fine granite composed of white Feldtspar and Quartz black Mica and Hornblende and in different parts blotches of large confused crystals of pale red calc: spar—also found Hornstone Porphyry, Glimmer Schiefer, both of black and green mica which latter inclined to chlorite Schiefer or the Lapis Ollaris so abundant in the vicinity of Inverary. I likewise observed some species of Whin Stone. At 4 o'clock we set out again and then quitted Loch Fyne—our road now lay among the Mountains which were lofty but destitute of trees. Small Rills and water falls frequently occurred and wood was only wanting to render the scene romantic and Picturesque. This district is called Glencoe[1]. On the road side was the Turf seat mentioned by Dr. Johnson with the stone inscribed Rest & be Thankfull. The former part of the day was dry but the rain now began to fall again. When we had gone about 11 Miles we came to a small but pleasant Loch bordered with some Trees called Loch Long and after having passed round the end of the Loch we came to a neat Inn called the New Inn pleasantly situate in the midst of a Plantation of Trees. The place itself is called Arrochan[2] Between Carrindow[3] and this place the Mountains appeared to be composed of the substance already mentioned viz: Lapis Ollaris, Glimmer & Chlorite Schiefer Quartz etc.

[1] Glen Croe   [2] [3] these should be Arrochar and Cairndow.

THURSDAY JULY 21ST   Our Inn at Arrochan afforded us excellent accommodations in respect to rooms, Beds and Provisions. After breakfast at about ½ past 10 o'Clock we set out and proceeded by East Tarbet a small village and along the banks of Loch Lomond which must have been beautiful had the weather not been so misty and rainy—at ½ past 2 o'Clock PM we arrived at Luss a small village pleasantly situate on the Banks of Loch Lomond. Here the country exhibited a very different appearance to what it had done at Tyn Drum or at Glencoe between Carrindow and Arrochan, for in those places little was to be seen but barren hills and Mountains, but here the country was cultivated and was well wooded with Ash, Oak and other Trees. Mr. Stuart the Minister to whom we had a letter was not at home and we therefore dined at the Inn which was neat and afforded us good accommodations. Near Luss are some quarries of slate or Argillaceous Schistus of the primitive kind, with which I found chlorite indurated which passed to Chlorite Schiefer and this again into the Argillaceous Schistus—the Chlorite and Chlorite Schiefer was also accompanied by white fat quartz in which were crystals of pale rose coloured Calcareous Spar, as well as a reddish brown metallic coloured Talcite. At Luss the characteristics of the Highlands had nearly disappeared for the country was well cultivated in most parts.

After dinner we set out and passed through a pleasant road with trees on each side by the Banks of the remaining part of Loch Lomond and proceeded through Bonille[1] a small Town in which much Linen or Cotton is bleached—near Bonille is a Doric Column erected to the Memory of Dr. Smollett by Mr. Smollet his nephew. We then crossed the Clyde[2] over a stone Bridge and entered Dumbarton where we supd and slept. Near Dumbarton we passed some quarries of bright red sandstone which appears to be generally used at Dumbarton for building, flag Pavements etc. I also observed a sand stone somewhat similar between Luss and Dumbarton near the River which the chaise forded, only this last stone contained fragments of chlorite schiefer. Near Dumbarton is the Castle which stands on two hills.

These hills are composed of a compact hard fine grained grey whin stone with some indurate pale brown clay and some soft Argillaceous Sandstone of the same colour. The Whin Stone at

[1] Bonhill.   [2] the river is the Leven, not the Clyde.

Dumbarton as well as that at Stirling and Edinburgh, exhibits vertical clefts and fissures and in its appearance whether in the Mass or in the columnar fragments approaches much to a resemblance with Basaltes.

Near Dumbarton is also a chain of hills which appeared to be of whin but I only could observe them at a distance. Dumbarton is 12 Miles from Luss and Luss is 12 or 14 from Arrochan.

On leaving Inverary I observed that the Kilts or Fillibegs were not in general use but gave place to Pantalons which are said to be of more ancient use in Scotland.

Dumbarton is a small town ill built.

FRIDAY JULY 22ND   After Breakfast set out from Dumbarton the road was good and lay by the side of the Clyde in what is called the Dale of Clyde which extends much beyond Dumbarton. The country in general is flat but well cultivated—on leaving Dumbarton at the distance of about 1 Mile we passed a chain of Whin Rocks apparently like that of the Castle Hill at Dumbarton viz. of a fine grained hard grey whin. At about 2 & $\frac{1}{2}$ Miles from Dumbarton is a House called Frisky Hall near which on the left or North side of the road leading to Glasgow is a Rock about 25 or 30 feet high composed of a reddish brown hard species of whin stone or (what I rather conceive to be) a species of indurated Wacke in which chlorite appears to be disseminated. This substance also in some parts of the rock forms a Porphyry by containing small crystals of white Feldtspar. This rock has like the other whins many fissures in various directions some of which are filled with white calcareous spar but the greater part are filled with a species of the Prehnite which was first noticed by Mr. Grotsche. The Prehnite is found either in flat masses cellular on both sides or partly assuming a Mamellonated figure generally radiated and composed of small prismatical crystals, sometimes so small and so approached to each other as to assume in some degree a compact texture almost resembling Calcedony. It is semi-transparent but when acted on by weather loses it by degrees so as to become opaque and then in appearance much resembles certain varieties of Sulphate of Barytes. The colour varies from pale apple green to yellowish green, pale yellow and white but when affected by the weather it is either of an ochry colour or of an opaque white. The Fracture in the direction of the Radii appears foliated but across the radii it seems to approach to the conchoidal form. The external lustre in some specimens well crystallized is like that of the Dauphine Prehnite but in others it is even inferior to that of many varieties of Calcedony. The internal lustre is pearly. It is not remarkably heavy.

It may be broken but not scratched with a knife and it emits sparks by collision with steel. It is frequently accompanied by Calc: Spar. Another substance is often found with it which is formed of long prismatical radii, is transparent or nearly so, and is white, of a pearly lustre and may be scratched with a knife altho' with some difficulty—but gives not any sparks with steel—This is a variety of Zeolite.

We continued our journey along the Dale of Clyde and after passing the Patrick Flour Mills we arrived at Glasgow and went to the Tontine Hotel.

SATURDAY JULY 23RD Breakfasted with Dr. Cleghorn Prof. of Chemistry to whom I had a letter from Dr. Hope of Edinburgh— afterwards went with Mr. Lawrie a friend of Dr. Cn. to see Dr. Anderson's[1] collection of Philos: Instruments etc. but could only see his Library Books, not very numerous (and what is called his collection of Minerals which however is totally undeserving of the name). Went afterwards to see the Infirmary, a noble stone Building erected under the inspection of Mr. Adams. The neatness and good internal arrangement corresponds with the external magnificence of the edifice. Saw the Library, not very voluminous nor magnificent— was much struck with two ridiculous pieces of sculpture of a bridling prim Lion & Unicorn on the outside stairs. Went with Dr. Cleghorn to see the Elaboratory—the apartments are good but badly provided with instruments etc. The Minerals chiefly rubbish, and the few which have been good are now nearly spoiled by negligence.

SUNDAY JULY 24TH Dined with Mr. Gordon & his Lady in company with Mr. Brown lately appointed Profr. of Experiml. Philosophy in the room of the late Dr. Anderson. Supped at home.

[1] Dr. John Anderson (1726-1796) succeeded Dr. Dick as Professor of Natural Philosophy at Glasgow University in 1757, founded by bequest the Andersonian Institute Glasgow, to which he left his library and apparatus. It was Anderson who gave Watt the job of repairing a model of the atmospheric engine, which belonged to the Natural Philosophy class, and on which Watt experimented with a separate condenser.

The City of Glasgow is extensive and contains many handsome houses particularly in the New Town—it is however much inferior in magnitude and magnificence to Edinburgh. It is pleasantly situate in the Dale of Clyde on the Banks of that river over which it has two stone Bridges. The country about it is flat, but well cultivated. The Cathedral (the only one now intire in Scotland) is a large pile of Gothic Architecture which never was completely finished. The rest of the churches are not remarkable excepting for the disproportional height and narrowness of their spires which resemble Rush Lights in clumsy candlesticks or as Mr. Jameson observes with me like erect Thread Papers. The College is an old building, the students are said to be about 200. Law is here the principal study as Physick is at Edinburgh, Divinity at Aberdeen and nothing at all at St. Andrews, at least as I am informed. Professor John Millar at Glasgow is regarded by every one (and by all account with much reason) as a very eminent Man.

The Buildings at Glasgow are of an excellent fine Grit or Free-stone—Very good Pit coal is raised in many places about Glasgow, the strata of which all dip towards the Bed of the Clyde on each side and often appear to the Day in the neighbouring Mountains. At about 5 Miles from the city is a celebrated Aqueduct on which a canal is conveyed so that Vessels are seen sailing above whilst carriages are passing underneath. This I did not visit.

MONDAY JULY 25TH   After Breakfast at ¼ before 10 oClock we set out from Glasgow—the road was near the Clyde in a level cultivated country. At about 3 Miles from Glasgow we stopped to see the Clyde Iron Works which belong to Messrs. Edingtons who have given a small share to Mr. Bigbie late of St. Petersburgh. These works are about ½ a Mile out of the road to the right or west and are near the river. They are extensive and have three Blast Furnaces each about 36 feet high by 15 in the widest part—when the works goes on well each of these Furnaces will produce about 25 Tons of Iron per week. They employ about 400 men. There are several Air Furnaces as at the other Iron Works and a small Blast Cone as at Carron for the Scrap Iron. The ore is brown Argillaceous Stone with calc: spar which with the coal is found in the neighbourhood. The coal is even raised within sight of the Works at less than ¼ of a Mile distance. The Lime Stone used as a Flux is hard and of a dark grey but not bituminous. At these works they cast and bore cannon of all sizes likewise all sorts of Vessels, Cylinders etc. Their Blowing Cylinders & Boring Machines are worked by the common Steam Engines.

We continued our route through a level country (at least for the chief part) and arrived at Hamilton a small Town which gives the title to the Duke of Hamilton who has a seat in the neighbourhood. Hamilton is 11 Miles from Glasgow.

Changed Horses and pursued our Journey through a country diversified with Hill & Dale, well wooded and cultivated. The road was chiefly near the Banks of the Clyde—passed a fine seat belonging to the Earl of Hyndford—at about 4 Miles before we reached Lanark we stopped to see Stone Byre one of the falls of the Clyde which is about 50 feet in Depth and is very beautiful and Picturesque. Reached Lanark a small Town by ¼ past 4 PM. After dinner went to see the Cotton Mills belonging to Mr. Dale. These are about 1 Mile from the Town and consist of 4 immense Buildings of 6 stories in which by Machines worked by a water wheel and attended principally by Children, cotton is carded and spun into yarn. In these Works above 400 Children are employed but it is said that in all Works belonging to Mr. Dale 1600 Persons are employed. Afterwards went to see Cora Lin waterfall of the Clyde about ½ a Mile from the Mills and also Bonnetin[1] falls ½ a Mile beyond Cora. These are in the lands of Sir Charles Lockhart Ross who has a fine seat near them. The country and cliffs on all sides are thickly covered with wood and these falls have a most beautiful and Romantic appearance—Cora is about 55 or 60 feet deep and Bonnetin about 40. Bonnetin is the first fall. Cora is the 2nd and Stone Byre the 3rd. Of these Cora appeared to me as the most beautiful.

Slept at Lanark. Lanark is 15 Miles from Hamilton.

TUESDAY JULY 26TH After Breakfast at ½ past 8 oClock we set out and passed thro' a country in great measure open, arrived at Douglas Mills 9 Miles from Lanark. Changed Horses and proceeded through a dreary country chiefly consisting of Heath and Moor ground— from the time we left Lanark we most commonly ascended and when we were at about 10 Miles from Douglas Mills the road became very hilly as it lay among high and barren Mountains. The more we

[1] Bonnington.

advanced the more dreary the country appeared and much resembled that about Tyn Drum excepting that it was if possible worse at and near the Lead Hills. The weather was abominably bad and it was difficult to say whether the Wind or the Rain was most violent. The road was much intersected by small Torrents of Water which came from the Hills in consequence of the heavy Rain. At 1 oClock we arrived at the Lead Hills 15 Miles from Douglas Mills—the appearance is dreary beyond description. There is a Village inhabited by the Miners and Mr. Sterling the Director[1] to whom I had a letter has a very good House.—He received us with great Hospitality and Politeness. We dined with him and found him a most pleasant well informed Man willing to communicate to us anything we desired to know.

The situation of the Lead Hills is very elevated being nearly 2,200 feet above the level of the Sea and it may be therefore reckoned as one of the highest if not the highest spot of ground in Great Britain which is cultivated. It is uncommonly subject to Stormy Weather in all Seasons for Wind and Snow prevail in Winter and Wind and Rain in summer. I found it exceptionally raw and cold and I experienced a considerable chilliness in my Back which I find most commonly attacks strangers on their arrival. The Lead Mines have been worked beyond tradition, but the first authentic account of them is about the time of Elizabeth. At present they belong to a Company of 16 Persons of whom the Earl of Hopetoun has a 6th chare which at times by Mr. Stirling's account will produce £6,000 so that the produce of the Mine now worked must be £36,000. The country of the Mine is a very hard Schistose clay, the leaves of which rise to the surface of the earth edgewise. The Vein (which consists of Galena principally) runs from North to South and dips to East at the rate of about $2\frac{1}{2}$ or 3 feet in a Fathom. The vein goes shelving down from the grass [see overleaf] and is worked as represented.

The principal ore is a fine brilliant broad foliated Galena which contains about 80 pct of Lead which by cupellation had been found to contain $5\frac{1}{2}$ oz of Silver in one Ton; it is not therefore worked for the silver. The Lead upon the average is worth £18 per Ton. The Matrix of the ore is Heavy Spar and sometimes Calc: Spar—the

[1] Rev. J. Moir Porteous in *"God's Treasure-House in Scotland"* says "the library (at Leadhills) was originally established by an overseer named Mr. Stirling, who was a famous mathematician."

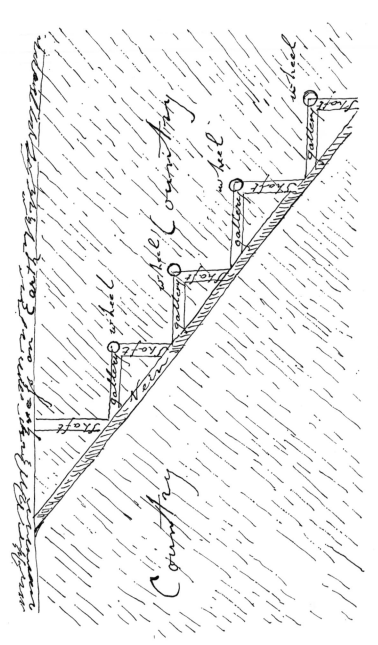

Leadhills Mine: A Section

vein varies from one to 2 inches to 11 or 12 feet in width, at present it is very large. This mine affords beautiful crystallizations of the white and yellow spathose lead also some coloured green and blue by copper. Brown Wadd is likewise found in great abundance and is now used by the Bleachers.

The Lead Ore is smelted on the spot and as they have the advantage of much Peat they permit the fuel to be in contact with the ore without prejudice to the produce. The total depth of the Mine is 167 fathoms each shaft is about 13 fathoms—there are not any footways and the miners descend and the ore is raised by Ropes and Wheels.

After dinner about 5 oClock we set out and changed Horses at Elvan Foot 5 Miles from the Lead Hills. We then proceeded through a bleak Mountainous and barren country, chiefly Peat Moors, and arrived by 9 in the evening at Moffat, 14 Miles, a neat Town as far as I could perceive. Here we supped and I then took leave of Mr. Jameson and set out in the Mail Coach at ½ past 12 PM and reached Carlisle 46 Miles from Moffat by 6 in the morning.

WEDNESDAY JULY 27TH The approach to Carlisle is through a flat country—the Weather continued bad therefore I did not venture out. The country about Carlisle is flat and the Town is by no means Handsome, few good houses are to be seen in it. The Castle is very shabby.

THURSDAY JULY 28TH Set out from Carlisle at ½ past 9 o'clock PM. Road good and the country open with a view of the distant Hills—arrived at Wigton a small neat Town 11 Miles by 12 o'clock. Changed Horses and set out for Cockermouth the Road was through a very open country—at about 5 Miles from Wigton passed some Coal Pits in Bolton Parish belonging to the Earl of Egremont. arrived at Cockermouth by ¼ past 3 oClock—after dinner called on Mr. Robertson at Dearham Row about 6 Miles from the Town. Cockermouth is 18 Miles from Wigton. The country about Cockermouth is very beautiful and the Town is large, neatly built and is situated on the banks of the river in a beautiful valley. The Castle is a fine ruin not very antient; part is inhabited by a farmer. It produces a very picturesque effect when viewed with the Town from the foot of the Bridge.

Within about 6 or 7 Miles of Cockermouth the roads were mended with a pale grey limestone. Slept at Cockermouth. The Sandstone about Wigton is of various shades of red like that about Birmingham

FRIDAY JULY 29TH After Breakfast set out for Whitehaven. The road was good and through a fine open country. On approaching Whitehaven there is on the left a view of the Cumberland Hills and on the right a fine view of the Sea and the Port of Whitehaven with the coast and hills of Scotland and the Isle of Man in the distance. Arrived at Whitehaven, 14 Miles, by 12 oClock, called on Mr. Sanderson (an American merchant and a friend of Mr. Johnstons of Byker). Whitehaven is a pretty large compact built Town—the collieries which chiefly belong to Ld. Lonsdale are numerous and may extend 3 or 4 Miles under the Sea. They are much incommoded with Fire Damps (more than at Newcastle) and are obliged to use Steel Mills instead of candles. Ld. Lonsdale has a seat called Whitehaven Castle near the Town. Dined at Whitehaven with Mr. Sanderson; paid a visit on board of an American ship—returned in the evening and slept at Cockermouth. Limestone and iron ore abound in the area.

SATURDAY JULY 30TH After Breakfast set out for Keswick, passed for about 4 Miles through an open country and then the road winded among the Mountains. These at the beginning appeared to be principally composed of a thick hard grey Schistus which with some difficulty gave Sparks with Steel. The opening to the valley in which Keswick is situate is very beautiful. On the way to Keswick called on the Revd. Mr. Wilkinson who lives at Ormathwaite at the foot of Skiddaw at about 1 & ½ Miles from Keswick. His house is situate in such a manner as to command a View of the whole length of the Lake with the Islands, Mountains, etc. etc. and the situation is esteemed one of the best in the neighbourhood of Keswick. Before dinner I accompanied Mr. W. in his Whisky to see Lowdore Waterfall and to the Grange at the entrance of Borrowdale both of which are beautiful and romantic. Dined with Mr. Wilkinson—saw Dr. Brownrigg the uncle of Mrs. W. who is now superannuated—he is the oldest Pupil of Boerhaave now living and his Diploma at Leyden is signed by Boerhaave, Linneus and S'Graverande. In the evening went to Friars Head at Keswick where I supped and slept. Keswick is 12 Miles from Cockermouth.

SUNDAY JULY 31ST   In the morning went to see Mr. Crosthwaites Museum—contains little that is worthy of notice, especially in respect to minerals. Afterwards went in a Boat on the Lake and viewed the coasts etc. etc. Dined with Mr. Wilkinson. Supped and slept at the Inn. The Mountains about Keswick appear to differ in their Materials—hard Schistus, Mandelstein, Quartz and Chlorite abound—also some species of Whin Stone.

MONDAY AUGUST IST Breakfasted at 7 oClock and set out at 8 to go and see the Mine of Plumbago or Black Lead. When I had passed about 4 Miles to the extremity of the Lake where Borrowdale begins at a place called the Grange, I stopped to take up with me in the chaise Mr. Caleb Fisher a principal farmer who lives there. We then proceeded through Borrowdale by a very bad Road among the Mountains and at length stopped at a small village called Seathwaite about 9 Miles from Keswick. This village is situate in Borrowdale and is to the S or rather to the S West of Keswick. Opposite to this village on a hill is the Mine called the Wadd Mine. (Wadd is the name by which Plumbago is generally known in this country). The path which leads from the village to the Mine is about $\frac{1}{2}$ a Mile in length and towards the upper part is very steep. This hill appears to be chiefly composed of a hard species of pale blue whin stone. Below the place which is now worked, about $\frac{1}{4}$ of a Mile are the remains of a shed which covered the old Mine (now abandoned). The present has been opened at different times since more than 26 years. The plumbago is found in Nodules accompanied by a loose Ochry Grit stone which however does not form strata but is said only to be seen with the Plumbago. I do not therefore believe that the Plumbago runs in Veins. altho' the People are of a different opinion. I am inclined to believe that the deception arises from the Plumbago being found at some length in certain clifts or fissures which have given the appearance of a vein which runs nearly North and South with an inclination towards the East from West. It is found at different depths from the grass to 70 yards. The last quantity was found at 2 fathoms below the surface and was of a good quality. They are now driving a Level on the surface nearly N & South but I think the Pits sunk in various places would be a better mode to try to find it. They employ 7 Men and the expences of the Mine are very little. Great loss falls on the Proprietors by the pilfering of the Men. The best Plumbago is now said to be worth £3-3-0 per lb?—upon the whole Plumbago seems to me to be found like Manganese viz: in bunches or nodules and it is not therefore very probable that it has or can form a regular Vein. The rubbish which is thrown away, I think, might afford Plumbago for Crucibles etc. etc. The Plumbago differs much in quality. The finest sort is compact without Pores and shines much when scraped with a knife. The worst sort is very dull and friable.

Mr. Hy Banks M.P. for Corfe in Dorsetshire has one half of this Mine, the remaining half is divided into 8 shares of which Sr. Jos. Banks has one. Borrowdale is very Romantic; near what is called the Castle Hill formerly a Roman Station (which is as you enter Borrowdale from Keswick) is a considerable quarry which affords a pale greenish Slate excellent for covering houses etc. etc.

Returned to Keswick and dined. Set out at ½ past 4 oClock for Low Wood at about 1 Mile from Keswick, from the Hill is a fine view of Bassenthwaite & Derwentwaters with the Vale of Keswick etc. The Views on most parts of the road were Picturesque and beautiful. Passed an heap of stones with a wall which separate Cumberland & Westmorland. The views of Grassmere and Rydal Water are very beautiful—passed Ambleside a small Town and arrived at Low Wood (18 Miles from Keswick) by ½ past 7.

Low Wood is a single Inn on the Banks of Windermere, most beautifully situate. I think upon the whole that Windermere is the most beautiful of all the Lakes—it is 15 miles long. Low Wood Inn was full and I was therefore obliged to go on to Kendal 12 Miles. The Hills about Windermere and in Westmorland appeared to me to be better wooded than those in Cumberland—perhaps or indeed most probably this arises from the difference of Soil, for the Mountains in these parts at least about Kendal consist chiefly of pale grey Limestone. Supped and slept at the Kings Arms, a good Inn.

TUESDAY AUGUST 2ND   After Breakfast set out from Kendal; on leaving the Town the ruins of the Castle have a Picturesque effect and the Town appears to advantage from the Castle Hill. Arrived at Burton a small Town 11 Miles from Kendal by ½ past 11 o'clock, changed Horses and proceeded through a well cultivated country which became nearly a plain near Lancaster, where we arrived by ½ past One. Lancaster is a considerable town and has many handsome Buildings. The New Stone Bridge and the Bridge Inn have a good effect. A small arm of the sea comes up to the Town. The Castle which which is on an eminence with the principal church is for the greater part rebuilding but the Entrance remains which is supposed to have been built by Edward the third, or John of Gaunt. Some other antient parts are also remaining as a Square Tower etc. etc. etc. Dined at the Kings Arms kept by one Culthwaite—the charges exhorbitant, the people uncivil and the whole concluded by their giving me a Diligence (which they wanted to return) instead of a Post Chaise altho' they had 6 in the yard. (Lancaster 11 Miles) here also they began to charge 1s 3d per Mile.

Set out at ½ past 2 o'clock and proceeded through cultivated but nearly flat country to a small Town called Garstang 11 Miles, where we changed Horses and went on to Preston—the country all the way was very flat. Preston is 11 Miles from Garstang; it is a very considerable Town. Ld. Derby has an handsome House in it. Supped and slept at the Bull a very considerable Inn.

WEDNESDAY AUGUST 3RD   After Breakfast set out at ½ past 9 oClock, road rough, the country open and well cultivated, arrived at Chorley (10 Miles) by ½ past 11 oClock. Chorley is a small Town near which is the seat of Sr Frank Standish whose Steward Mr. Tatham or Tatem has the disposal of the Carbonate of Barytes formerly worked in the neighbourhood[1]. Changed Horses at Chorley and proceeded over a very bad road paved with large stones to Bolton (11 Miles) the country to this place was open and beautiful. Changed Horses and proceeded through a most beautiful open country to Manchester 11 Miles from Bolton where we arrived by ½ past 4 oClock. From Lancaster to Manchester the drivers and in general the people at the Inns were uncivil and negligent to a degree beyond what I ever met with.

About Chorley are some coal Pits and between Bolton and Manchester are others. At Chorley Micaceous Grit seemed to prevail as I have observed it do to in other countrys which afforded Coal. Near Manchester the soil is sandy. Slept at the Bridgewater Arms, a large Inn but the people Negligent and exhorbitant in their charges. In the

[1] This is the mineral Witherite so named by Werner, after Dr. Withering a botanist and mineralogist of Birmingham, who discovered it in the mines of Anglezark. These are in the parish of Bolton, Lancashire, in the mineral royalty of Sir Frank Standish (at the time of Hatchett's visit) of Duxbury near Chorley. Reference can be made to "The Anglezark Lead Mines." I. A. Williamson. *Mining Magazine.* 108 (1963). pp. 133-139.

evening I called on Mr. Henry the celebrated Apothecary at Manchester and found him a very pleasant and communicative Man.

THURSDAY AUGUST 4TH Manchester is very extensive and has great numbers of Elegant Houses etc. Its manufactures etc. are well known.

Set out at ½ passed 12 and went through a fine country more inclosed than that on the other side of Manchester. Arrived at Altringham 8 Miles from Manchester by 2 o'clock. Altringham is a small Town—dined and set out again the road good and the country inclosed and finely cultivated. Arrived at Northwich a pretty considerable Town by 5 oClock being 12 Miles from Altringham. Supped and slept at the Crown Inn.

FRIDAY AUGUST 5TH Northwich is noted for the Salt Mines and Works in its neighbourhood. It is said that there are more than 20 Salt Pits or Mines which belong to different Persons or Companies. These vary in depth but that called the Dukes Pit is the deepest and is about 105 yards. Those Pits which are near the river it is observed are liable in the course of time to fall in. The superincumbent strata consist chiefly of sand and clay—the Salt is white and pellucid, or red or brown. It is blowed with gunpowder in the mines (of late years) by which it is procured at a less expence than formerly and it is raised in Buckets by means of a whim and horses. A great Number of Vessels are always at N to be laden with this salt. A considerable quantity of water flows through these Salt Mines which is pumped up by the means of Wind Mills into certain Reservoirs from which it is drawn into large Evaporating Pans of Iron about 12 feet square by 1½ feet deep. It is then by evaporation at length brought to that fine granulated state called Basket Salt. It is worthy of note that by digging in any part almost about Northwich Salt is to be found, but in many places they are prevented from arriving at the Salt by a Quicksand which is generally at about 15 yards from the surface. This Quicksand most commonly or always occurs and often puts a total stop to the proceedings. The Salt both of the Mines and of the Pans is of a good quality. The Salt most frequently is in Masses which have a crystalline fracture, the facets of which are larger than those of the Grey Salt found at Wickerzka in Poland.

Set out and passed through open country for the greater part—

arrived at Chester 18 Miles from N by 2 oClock. Dined and in the evening I found myself so unwell that I consulted Dr. Haygarth who ordered me to take an emetic.

SATURDAY AUGUST 6TH, SUNDAY AUGUST 7TH, MONDAY AUGUST 8TH, TUESDAY AUGUST 9TH I remained more or less indisposed during these days but on the Tuesday was much better. Chester is a pretty large City but is not handsome. The Cathedral has nothing remarkable excepting the Chapter House which I did not see. The Principal Streets have a covered way on each side something in the manner of Piazza's—there is also a Pleasant walk round the city on the Walls. The new Prison is an handsome stone building. The Castle has nothing remarkable unless it is part of a Tower said to have been built by Julius Caesar. Chester is in a Plain. The prevalent substance on which Chester is built and about it is a red ferruginous grit—according to Dr. Haygarth this grit prevails throughout Cheshire.

WEDNESDAY AUGUST 10TH Set out from Chester after Breakfast the road was very good and through a beautiful country. Arrived at Wrexham 12 Miles from Chester, a pretty large Town—the Spire of the church is very beautiful—changed Horses and proceeded by a fine road and country to Ellesmere a moderately large Town 12 Miles from Wrexham. Dined and set out—passed some pretty lakes called the Great Mere, the White Mere and the Little Mere, which belong to Sir W. W. Wynne. Part of the road was very good but part of it was sandy. The country was fine and well cultivated. Arrived in the evening at Shrewsbury 16 Miles from Ellesmere. The red grit appeared to continue to Shrewsbury.

Shrewsbury is a large Town (near which is a castle belonging to Mr. Pulteney) but my Indisposition prevented me from properly seeing it. In the evening I became worse and passed a sleepless night.

THURSDAY AUGUST 11TH I was so unwell in the morning that I sent for Dr. Darwin junr. Towards Noon I became better and after dinner determined to proceed to Coal Brook Dale. The country is fine about Shrewsbury which seems to me to be principally built in a Plain. Crossed the Severn over a Bridge—the Corn here was abundant and the road very good. Arrived at Coal Brook Dale by 7 in the evening. C. B. Dale is 13 Miles from Shrewsbury. Had difficulty to get a bed at the Tontine Inn as the Prince of Orange was expected, who actually arrived at 10 oClock.

FRIDAY AUGUST 12TH After Breakfast proceeded to Bridgenorth 8 Miles, the Road hilly but the country is fine. Bridgenorth is a large Town, the hills which are near it appeared to be principally composed of the red Grit. Changed Horses and proceeded by sandy and hilly Road which however became better when about midway towards Kidderminster—the country (particularly near K.) is very beautiful and open. Near K the Road appeared to be repaired with a sort of whin stone—dined at Kidderminster which is a large Town chiefly remarkable for the Manufacture of Carpets. Set out after dinner and went by an excellent road through a beautiful open Country to Worcester 14 Miles from K. In a former part I have noticed that the red grit prevails about Worcester and by this road it extends from Chester to Shrewsbury and so to Worcester but not to Coal Brook Dale—at least I did not observe it.

SATURDAY AUGUST 13TH After Breakfast set out passed through Pershore a large Town 7 Miles from Worcester and proceeded from thence to Bengworth a pretty considerable Town 16 Miles from Worcester. The Road was good through a fine open country. On this side the hard blue marle prevailed from Worcester similar to that which I have noticed about Tewkesbury—the soil was however red in many places. Dined at Bengworth.

After dinner set out again; at about 4 Miles from Bengworth the blue Marle changed to a yellowish Lime Stone in texture somewhat resembling Bath Stone. At about 7 Miles from Morton some traces of white Limestone or rather Chalk appeared—arrived at Morton a small Village which I believe is 12 Miles from Bengworth. Changed Horses and proceeded by Chipping Norton a large well built Town to Chapel House, a large commodious Inn which stands by itself 9 Miles from Norton. The country about Chapel House is very fertile all the way from Norton is very fertile and beautiful.
NB The country is open all the way from Norton.

SUNDAY AUGUST 14TH After Breakfast set out and went to Woodstock 10 Miles and from thence to Oxford 8 Miles. Dined at Oxford and then went to Benson 12 Miles, from thence to Henley 11 Miles, to Maidenhead 9 Miles, to Cranford Bridge 14 Miles and arrived at Hammersmith 10 Miles by ¼ before 9 oClock in the evening. Yellowish Calcareous Grit prevails as far as Oxford and about to Heddington near Shotover where the Selenite is found. Between Benson and Henley chalk appears and continues to about the 27 Mile Stone from London. Gravel then prevails after which no further change is visible on this side of London.

INDEX

Books on Cornish mining and industrial history

THE STANNARIES

G. R. LEWIS

A study of the mediaeval tin miners of Cornwall and Devon, including the technical development of early mining and smelting under the jurisdiction of the Stannaries.

Demy octavo . 299 *pages* . 45s.

AN INTRODUCTION TO THE GEOLOGY OF CORNWALL

R. M. BARTON

This book is the first detailed and balanced account of the geology of the county in a single volume. Whilst appealing primarily to students, it will prove of interest also to those who would know more of a subject that is the key to much of Cornwall's scenery and character.

Demy octavo . 168 *pages* . 20 *plates* . 4 *maps* . 30s.

A HISTORY OF THE CORNISH CHINA-CLAY INDUSTRY

R. M. BARTON

A detailed history of the china-clay and china-stone industry of Cornwall—one of the most important and individual extractive industries in Great Britain today.

Royal octavo . 212 *pages* . 35 *plates* . 20 *maps and other illustrations* . 42s.

THE HARVEYS OF HAYLE

EDMUND VALE

The official history of the notable Harvey & Company—master engineers, ship-builders and merchants in Cornwall since 1779; a record of industrial enterprise unsurpassed in nineteenth century Cornwall.

Royal octavo . 356 *pages* . 35 *plates* . 8 *maps and other illustrations* . 50s.

ARTHUR WOOLF 1766-1837: THE CORNISH ENGINEER

T. R. HARRIS

A long overdue biography of the man who, during the greatest era of the Cornish engine from 1810 to 1830, was the county's leading engineer.

Demy octavo . 112 *pages* . 7 *plates and other illustrations* . 25s.

'MONGST MINES AND MINERS

J. C. BURROW

A classic series of underground mining scenes taken by flash-light, illustrating the methods of working Cornish mines in the 1890's.

Crown quarto . 40 *pages* . 24 *plates* . 10s. 6d.

A COMPENDIUM OF BRITISH MINING

J. Y. WATSON

A reprint of a classic of 1843, including notes on the principal mines in Cornwall, together with a glossary of mining terms, etc.

Demy octavo . 84 *pages* . 10s. 6d.

A HISTORY OF TIN MINING AND SMELTING
IN CORNWALL   D. B. BARTON

An account of tin mining and smelting in Cornwall—both hitherto unchronicled as industries—from 1800 to the present day.

Royal octavo . 300 pages . 37 plates . 6 maps etc . 60s.

THE REDRUTH & CHASEWATER RAILWAY:
1824-1915   D. B. BARTON

A detailed history of this highly individual 4' gauge Cornish mineral railway and of the copper mines it was built to serve in the great Gwennap mining district. [Second edition.]

Demy octavo . 104 pages . 12 plates . 5 maps . 12s. 6d.

THE CORNISH BEAM ENGINE   D. B. BARTON

A survey of its history and development in the mines of Cornwall and Devon from before 1800 to the present day. Chapters are included on engines used not only for pumping but also for winding and stamping ore, for working man-engines, etc.

Demy octavo . 286 pages . 48 plans . 32 plates . 45s.

A GUIDE TO THE MINES OF WEST
CORNWALL   D. B. BARTON

An introduction to the larger and more interesting of the tin, copper and lead mines of western Cornwall, outlining their position and history.

Crown octavo . 52 pages . 18 maps and other illustrations . 6s. 6d.

EAST WHEAL ROSE   H. L. DOUCH

A history of East Wheal Rose, greatest of the lead mines of Cornwall, including the cloudburst disaster that flooded the mine in 1846, the little-known beginnings of the mine, and the final financially disastrous re-working in the 1880's.

Crown octavo . 84 pages . 5 plates . 2 maps . 8s. 6d.

THE PENTEWAN RAILWAY 1829-1918   M. J. T. LEWIS

The history of Cornwall's only true narrow-gauge line, the 2' 6" gauge Pentewan Railway built in 1829 to connect the port of that name with the china-clay producing area north of St. Austell.

Demy octavo . 58 pages . 10 plates . 5 maps . 8s. 6d.

Published by

D. BRADFORD   **BARTON LTD**

TRURO BOOKSHOP   TRURO CORNWALL